The Art of the Structural Engineer

The Art of the
Structural Engineer

Bill Addis

Artemis

First published 1994 by
Artemis London Limited
55 Charlotte Road
London EC2A 3QT

British Library Cataloguing in
Publication
A CIP record for this book is available
from the British Library

ISBN 1874 056 41 2 (London)
ISBN 3 7608 8430 X (Zürich)

Edited by Annie Bridges
Designed by Jonathan Moberly
with Kevin Whelan
Printed and bound in England by
Smart Arts, Brighton

Contents

Foreword

This book is intended for architects and young engineers. It has many origins, but most directly arose out of a series of exhibitions I curated on 'The Structural Engineer's Contribution to Contemporary Architecture', sponsored by the Building Centre Trust and first shown at the Building Centre's premises in London. Two travelling exhibitions have since been hosted by most British schools of architecture and four departments of engineering.

My second reason for writing the book lies embedded in the first – why have these exhibitions been seen by far more architects than engineers? I have long been concerned that engineering students are not inspired to take as active an interest in design as students of architecture – yet the construction industry provides employment for more design engineers than architects. Those who become engineers seem nowadays to do so only because of a talent for maths and physics at school, not as the result of an enthusiasm for designing and making things. Is it, perhaps, no coincidence that the *Yellow Pages* contains the following entry: 'Boring – see Civil Engineers'?

Thirdly, I have observed in many architects, both students and professionals, a phobia and and a sense of mystique about structures and materials, concerning both how they behave and how they are manufactured. This phobia often manifests itself as insecurity – why else should architects, even talented or famous ones, be so reticent about acknowledging the contribution made to their projects by structural engineers? I have seen it come as a revelation to some architects that a useful understanding of many aspects of structural engineering can be gained without recourse

Art is solving problems which cannot be formulated before they have been solved. The search goes on, until a solution is found, which is deemed to be satisfactory. There are always many possible solutions, the search is for the best – but there is no best – just more or less good.

Ove Arup

to complex maths and engineering science. With a better understanding of structures and materials, architects would be able to get far more out of the engineers with whom they work, and to do so without feeling that they are giving away advantages to the opposition.

Finally, there is my own enthusiasm for structures and design, which began when very young with designing and making engineering objects from Meccano and buildings with Bayko. There were also the *Meccano Magazine*, the cutaway how-it-works pictures in the *Eagle* comic, and books from the 1930s with such marvellous titles as *Engineering Wonders of the World* and *The Wonder Book of Engineering Wonders*. Here you could see pictures of 'natives using long-stroke riveting hammers for bridge construction in India' and 'the Bucyrus steam shovel holding thirty-four men'. You could read of 'the romance of the lifting magnet' and of the engineer as builder who, in 1904, was able to erect 'the steel cage of the New Phelan Building, San Francisco (329 by 296 by 205 feet) … in seventy-five working days'.

There is a crucial difference between these old books and what we find today. Then engineering artefacts were always portrayed as the products of man's efforts, skills and progress. There is no mention of that impersonal thing called 'technology' which is what we nowadays hear is responsible for all our aircraft, computers, bridges and buildings. No wonder fewer people now regard engineering as a challenging and rewarding career.

But back to design. Even the books from that lost, romantic age focused mainly on the making of engineering artefacts – the reader would have gained little or no idea of how the machines or structures were designed. This is just one of many ways in which the activity of design is often rendered invisible, and which together contribute to the difficulty people have in understanding just what design engineers do. In a world now dominated by marketing and image creation, it is vital that engineers devote more of their energies to publicising the nature of their skills in order to sell their services. Unfortunately, most design engineers seem to be too busy designing, too modest to undertake self-publicity or lacking in communication skills – or all three.

We live now in an era when more and more people are trying to ensure that better buildings are built by firing quiverfuls of management techniques at 'the design process'. It is important not to forget that the best way to get better buildings is for clients to employ good designers and to pay them enough to think carefully about every aspect of the design – and that includes how the

  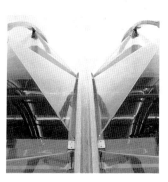

building will be built and maintained – before construction begins.

I believe all these matters are connected. I also believe it is important that people, especially architects and engineers, should have a good idea of what structural engineers do and understand something of the nature of good design. Yet, unlike in architecture, there are few books which celebrate good engineering. I hope this one will help render comprehensible and visible what is so often poorly understood and overlooked.

Bill Addis September 1994

Some philosophy

The Art of the Structural Engineer is about what structural designers do and how they do it well. One barrier to understanding any skill is that those who can do it well make it look easy. This book tries to convey what it is that engineers do which seems to be so very difficult for non-engineers to appreciate. Ultimately, however – as with the art of juggling – you only find out what it really involves when you try to do it yourself.

It is many people's perception that structural engineers merely ensure that an architect's design for a building will stand up and be safe, and that this involves a process requiring a great many calculations of stresses and deflections. Engineers do indeed do this, but they do much more besides. Architect and structural engineer usually work together closely during the entire process of developing the design of a building from the early concept stage through to the level of fine detail and construction. They are equal parents to their child and, like all parents, they make different contributions.

Another misconception is that engineering design has a certain inevitability about it – if it is based on scientific laws, how can there be any room for choice and subjectivity? This notion is reinforced by all the rational explanations and calculations which engineers need to produce as justification for their various decisions. But the convergence and objectivity of these later stages only commence after the earlier, highly divergent and turbulent stage of the design process during which all members of the design team propose, compare, reject and develop alternative ideas.

The engineer creatively combines various threads of thought, some contradictory and incompatible, to arrive at a specific prod-

Structure

You cannot have an engineering structure which is not made of a material, nor a material which is not in the form of a structure. It was Galileo, in 1638, who first clearly distinguished these two concepts and introduced the idea of stress in a material. He used them to argue against the view held 'by very many intelligent people' that the strength of a rope diminishes with its length. These people were, of course, correct, but not for the right reason. He exposed this fallacy by distinguishing between the weakness in a rope due to smaller area of cross-section and one due to fibres of an inferior quality: a longer rope is usually weaker than a shorter one because there is a higher probability of it containing one of these weaknesses, not simply because it is longer.

Robert Hooke followed some forty years later with his famous Law and introduced the concept of the stiffness of a material, as distinct from a structure made of that material. More recently, the waters have become rather muddied again with composite materials such as fibreglass and concrete containing steel bars, and with our knowledge of molecules. At the atomic scale all materials are structures, rather like a great many balls linked by springs. At the millimetre scale a material may be considered as entirely homogenous; in turn, pieces of a material may be linked together to form a structure such as a truss or fabric. Finally, if the truss or fabric is of sufficient extent, it may be convenient to think of it once again as homogenous.

Structure is all about doing more with less – using less material to support a given load or enclose a given volume, or making a

The profession [of structural engineering] does not attract young people because it is considered to be neither high-tech nor creative – though it is, unlike any other profession, both.

Jörg Schlaich

Art I assume to be any direction of the practical intellect to making things.

Alan Harris

uct. These threads arise from many origins – an understanding of engineering science, knowledge of the behaviour of actual materials and structures, experience of the construction process and, of course, the individual's own successes and failures. The engineer who is master of the scientific principles can have great freedom in making use of different materials, structural actions and construction techniques, and can bring as much creativity and subjectivity to a project as an architect.

Later in the book we look at how structural engineers helped to create some of the buildings they have worked on. But first, let us explore the nature of our subject a little with some talk of structure, which means different things to different people; of the nature of structural design, which is different from design carried out by an architect; of the sometimes harmonious, sometimes discordant relationship between engineer and architect; and of why some structures are acclaimed as good structures, others not.

stiffer or stronger object without using more material. Many structural engineers are fascinated by the whole idea of minimum weight structures, though they are generally used only in special circumstances such as aerospace structures or long-span roofs. More often it is a matter of balancing structural performance with the cost of achieving it; many more resources are needed to design and manufacture a structure with less weight, and this follows the law of diminishing returns – saving the first 10 per cent is easier than the next.

Structure is also a matter of scale. All manner of properties change as structures get bigger (Galileo helped us understand this too) and they do not all change at the same rate. Many an architect has been disappointed to learn that the balsa-wood and card structure he has made will not work when the span becomes many tens of metres.

Finally, structure is about choosing appropriate materials which can be made into suitable pieces and joined together so that the different elements are linked to form an effective whole.

We all have a feel for structure, but we cannot experience it directly like a smell. We can feel load through our muscles, although this can be misleading since our muscles get tired whereas loads and structures do not. We can sense movement too, either visually or through our sense of touch and the kinaesthetic feelings in our limbs. It might be argued that we can sense stress in some circumstances: a force applied by a drawing pin will cause pain but by a thumb will not; yet a sharp needle can sometimes penetrate the flesh without causing pain.

Our sense of structure comes from combining primary sensations and somehow interpreting them. Thus, we can sense stiffness as a relationship between force and movement, stability as a relationship between the weight of an object and the force needed to overturn it. Similarly, we build up a picture of structural or material properties such as strength, ductility and brittleness, the instability of a strut or even the structural advantages of folding a thin sheet. We come to know such things when we are very young, playing with wooden blocks and paper aeroplanes. We need to prove nothing to ourselves – 'I know that steel is stronger than timber' – but we cannot impart this knowledge to someone else.

Although we may all have such a feel for structure, we might not be conscious of it. Some of us may have developed a better sense of structure than others, but we might find it difficult to talk about such a skill. It is interesting to note this lay feel for structures in various words for flying buttress: German – *Strebebogen* (striving

order is spatial, musical or verbal. While anyone can perceive a structure, it starts to get interesting when we look at who is perceiving it and how they think and talk about the perception, and how they remember it or store it in the form of knowledge. Perceiving a structure is an active process and utterly dependent on the eye and brain of the person involved.

Even perceiving structure as geometry can involve interpretation. Ellipses, squares, cones and pyramids have geometric properties which are not immediately apparent to the untrained eye, such as how they can be easily subdivided and how they might appear from a different viewpoint. There are also relationships within and between shapes such as symmetry, proportion, harmony, and the consequences of two shapes intersecting. Shapes have cultural significance too. Triangles and circles have long been linked with an idea of perfection, both in a religious context and elsewhere. Certain geometric proportions were seen by Greek and medieval philosophers as the key to explaining the way the world worked, much as we nowadays use physics, biology and chemistry to explain natural phenomena. Geometrical forms can remind us of other artefacts with those shapes. In a building an architect might wish to evoke something by association – a floor structure similar to the jack-arch structures ubiquitous in 19th-century warehouses and mills, or a Roman barrel vault – with no intention that it should work structurally in the original manner.

To see a structure in geometrical terms is to be able to build a mathematical model of it and be able to manipulate and test it in an abstract way. Over the last few centuries mathematicians and

The positive role for the engineers' genius and skill [is] to use their understanding of materials and structure to make real the presence of the materials in use in the building, so that people warm to them, want to touch them, feel a sense of the material itself and of the people who made and designed it. To do this we have to avoid the worst excesses of the industrial hegemony. To maintain the feeling that it was the designer, and not industry and its available options, that decided, is one essential ingredient of seeking a tactile, <u>traces de la main</u> solution.

Peter Rice

arc); French – *arc boutant* (pushing arc); Spanish – *arbotante* (throwing arc).

We all experience structures in other ways too. We can see the materials they are made of, how strong they are and how light. We can see their form, both in man-made and naturally occurring structures such as trees, shells and flower petals. At one level we perceive these simply as geometrical shapes; at another we might imbue them with qualities of cultural, historical or psychological significance. We might also interpret them in terms of the concepts of engineering science.

Structure, then, is an abstract quality. It needs presence in the real world to be fully apprehended – what the structure is made of is important, as is where it is, what it is doing and who is apprehending it. Structure, in a general sense, is a relationship between various entities which displays a certain order and lack of randomness. To perceive order requires intelligence, whether the

scientists have invented another branch of mathematics – statics – in terms of which we can build other models of real-world objects. These models are founded, first of all, on geometry, but also contain information about loads and properties of materials so that they can simulate the response of materials to loads. This formal language of statics employs precisely defined concepts such as force, stress and stiffness, and various structural paradigms such as beams, arches and trusses. And here is where the difficulties and confusions can begin, for most of these concepts share words with our everyday language. The engineer's beam or arch is far more precisely and mathematically defined than the everyday word; conversely, what a non-engineer describes as an arch, beam or truss may, or may not, work as such in the engineer's sense of the word. Even two engineers may differ – one may describe a structure as a stiffened arch, another as a curved truss; they might even use different mathematical models to investigate its structural behaviour.

Architect and engineer will, then, interpret what they see in a structure in different ways – and these differences are not superficial. Their concept of structures is different and this affects the very thoughts and ideas they are likely to have. An architect will tend to conceive building forms either in terms of simple geometric shapes such as arcs, squares, spheres, cylinders and planes, and various man-made objects, or in terms of natural forms, which usually cannot be defined using simple geometry – bubbles, leaves, flowers, bones, ripples and so on.

Engineers, in addition, have their own set of preferred geometric forms which have their origins in the mathematical models found in structural science. An I- or an inverted T-shape are efficient cross-sections for a beam; depending on the material and how it is manufactured, efficient cross-sections for a column might be a solid circle, a tube, an H or a +. In order to use the minimum amount of material, beams and columns should taper as a parabola or paraboloid from their centres to the ends. Trusses need to be made up of triangles, sometimes of identical shape and size, sometimes changing. Suspension structures (and arches, inverted) feature catenaries or parabolas. Shells are usually made in the form of paraboloids, hyperboloids or hyperbolic paraboloids, but may also be elliptical, spherical, cylindrical or even have the form of a Lemniscate of Bernoulli (as in the Bank of England printing works at Debden).

A common thread among these engineers' forms is that they seldom occur naturally to architects – and even if they do, they are likely to be favoured for their geometry rather than their structural

would, for instance, be difficult to appreciate the significance of the difference between statically determinate and indeterminate (redundant) structures. This is especially true of the difference between bracing a structure by triangulation as opposed to portal or Vierendeel action, or the idea that particularly stiff parts of a structure attract load away from other less stiff load paths through a structure. It might be possible to understand the differences between linear and non-linear materials: most materials are linear while they remain elastic in compression and tension, steel becomes non-linear when it deforms in a ductile way in tension or compression. A stone wall and a cable are both non-linear in another way; the first will carry compression but no tension, the second the converse. However, a non-engineer is less likely to comprehend the effect these differences can have on the stability of structures, their behaviour under alternating loads, the way they will fail or even collapse, the accuracy of predictions of their safety, and so on. Finally, and sadly, the subtleties of prestressed structures are also likely to remain something of a mystery to the non-engineer.

There is also the important matter of detail. Basic conceptions of structural behaviour (truss, beam, arch, etc.) are one thing, but most problems tend to arise at the level of detail – often minute detail. A cable is one of the easiest structures to conceive, but making it work – in terms of achieving the required strength, stiffness and bending properties, having suitable dynamic behaviour, corrosion, creep and fatigue characteristics, and manufacturing it to precisely the right length and fixing the ends – is a complex matter

 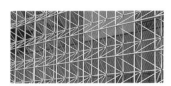 

efficiency. Another feature they share is that they can all be defined using relatively simple mathematical equations. This is essential if the engineer is to be able to build the mathematical model which will be needed to try to predict their structural behaviour. Many natural structures find their own form and do not fall into this category – spiders' webs, soap-film bubbles, taut nets. While small versions of such forms are easy to make, it has only recently become possible to create large-scale versions for use in buildings. In the late 1950s Frei Otto began developing various ways of scaling-up data gathered from small hanging models, but the real leap forward came when computers became powerful and quick enough to simulate the natural process of letting a structure find its own form.

Without a reasonable knowledge of the mathematical models used to represent loads, materials and structures, only a limited understanding of structures and their behaviour is possible. It

which few architects can, or need to, understand. The same is true of fabric and shell structures, the precise shape of which are sometimes believed to be a matter of relatively free choice.

It is thus inevitable that an architect, largely unaware of many of these complexities, will make choices which sometimes do not make for easy and cost-effective structural solutions. Perhaps most serious are the problems they can inadvertently cause by not understanding the significance of such secondary effects as stress concentrations and eccentrically applied loads which can make a structure prone to torsional instability.

There is, perhaps, a third position to defend, intermediate between what has been characterised as the engineering way of seeing structures and that of the architect, who sees them purely for their geometric, spatial, enclosing and iconographic functions. There are architects who incorporate the structure of a building into the architecture in more than a merely functional way. Derek

Sugden has made the 'irreverent but not necessarily irrelevant' observation that, between architectural form and engineering structure, there is 'archi-structure' – summarised, perhaps, as the architect's idea of what a functional structure of a building ought to look like. As with all ideas, it can be executed both well and poorly, and this book contains many examples of the former. But the phenomenon is hardly new: the ribs of late Gothic vaults do not carry loads in the same way as their early Gothic ancestors did; in the later fan vault, the ribs have virtually become appliqué.

What, then, do engineers see when they imagine or look at a structure? Broadly, they see patterns of loads which the structure must withstand; and they see load paths which conduct these loads through the structure to the foundations and the earth. The idea of the load path is very powerful, but it is perhaps a more nebulous concept than non-engineers might imagine. Sketches of load paths usually show lines and arrows, yet nothing actually flows. (A theoretician would say that it is, in fact, momentum which flows along a load path, but that's a bit obscure and doesn't help us here.) Also, the structure may be transmitting the load at one point along the load path by working in bending, at another by working in shear and at another by working in compression. Furthermore, in a finished building it is virtually impossible to affirm that loads actually are being carried along certain paths rather than others; and it may not even be certain that a structure is carrying these loads by means of one combination of structural actions rather than another. This is especially true of old buildings which will not now be working in precisely the way they were conceived to work by

ure of just one component or to progressive collapse. They see the behaviour of each element and sub-assembly in isolation, and of the entire structure as a whole. They see parts of the structure which might give rise to difficulties – insufficient or too much stiffness, and stress concentrations and instability (especially the inadequate bracing of frames and thin sheets of material required to carry compression).

Engineers see structures not as static objects but as things that move, and in various ways – deflection due to loads; movement caused by thermal expansion, foundation settlement and creep; movement at joints, which must be prevented, permitted, or allowed with some restraint in twelve possible degrees of freedom; movement in vibrations at the structure's natural frequency; and movement associated with the tolerances on component dimensions to allow them to be assembled yet be neither too loose nor too tight.

Structural engineers see the potential for materials to corrode or otherwise degrade, and to cause problems when they expand in warm weather or lose vital structural properties in a fire. They will also see a structure as having properties which impinge on the building envelope, the internal environment and the professional domains of the services engineer – thermal mass, U-values, sound absorption and so on. Finally, the structural engineer will see a structure as something that has to be built easily, cheaply, and quickly, and in a manner which is stable and safe at all times during construction.

Looking at a structure is an active process, even at the level of

There is certainly no rule or recipe leading to good form, but there are means and ways towards it. The engineer, if he is interested, can contribute to it with variety and lightness. We must evoke the structural engineer's interest in this most inspiring part of his profession, beginning at the university level. I know this is difficult to achieve because an engineer first has to learn a great deal more than the university can offer, before he is able to do creative designs. It is a fact that he even loses the unbiased approach to form and shape with which he enters the university. After some time, he will only design what he is able to analyse, which is not very much. The university must bring him over this hurdle.

Jörg Schlaich

the original designer (and may never have done so) – structural surveys depend heavily on experience and judgement. What can be said with complete confidence is that, if a building is standing, there will be a satisfactory series of load paths. If the building has survived other types of load during its life, such as heavy machinery or a hurricane, then it is also certain that, at that time, there must have been satisfactory loads paths for those loads too, though this may no longer be the case. These matters become of great concern as soon as someone proposes disturbing or removing parts of a building to effect repairs or adapt it to a new use and meet modern regulations.

As well as different structural actions along the various load paths, engineers can imagine the structure's likely behaviour under various loads – changing levels of stress, deflections and, for each combination of loads, likely collapse mechanisms. They see the inherent lack of safety in a structure which is vulnerable to the fail-

the words we use. In describing structures we need to categorise them. Engineers are likely to do this according to how they work, or think they work. Structures can be grouped into families or types, for instance, when we decide which word to use to describe them. This process of classification, or taxonomy as the biologists call it, is not necessarily objective; what one engineer sees as a truss, another might see as a beam with holes in (a perforated beam model was used when the Warren truss was first analysed in 1851). In general, engineers tend to categorise structures according to which mathematical model and technique of structural analysis they might use, although even this approach is becoming confused by computer programs which look only at local stresses and have a flagrant disregard for the principles of structure.

The following classification represents one perspective on structure; readers may have, or can develop, another for their own purposes.

Basic structural actions			
	1-dimension	2-dimension	3-dimension
Compression	column strut wall	buttress flying buttress arch barrel vault	ribbed vault fan vault dome thin shells grid shells
Tension	tie cable hanger	catenary suspension bridge	shear-free (bubbles, cable nets) shear-resistant (fabrics, membranes)
Truss	n/a	statically determinate (pin-jointed, Warren truss, etc) statically indeterminate (redundant members, rigid joints, etc)	space truss lattice truss
Bending	beams one-way slab portal frames Vierendeel	grillage two-way slabs (flat, ribbed, coffered, etc.)	frames Kubik 'truss'
Shear	plate action shear wall	plate action shear wall	folded plates torsion

Complex structural actions	
Combinations	post and lintel, column and beam, tied arch, jack arch
Composite materials	grp, grc, fibreglass, plywood, chipboard, etc.
Composite action	reinforced concrete; steel beam, metal decking with shear studs; concrete-encased steel column with shear studs
Stiffening	self weight (for arch or catenary) trussing (for beam, arch or strut) truss action (for arch or catenary) beam action (for arch or catenary) folded plate action (for flat plate or thin shell)
Stabilising	geometry (bricks and voussoirs in walls, masonry arches, domes, etc.) tie downs (for masts, etc.) pre-stressing (self weight in gravity structures, tension and compression in strut and tie structures, tension in membranes)
Bracing	by triangulation by cross bracing or K-bracing (for frames) by portal action, rigid joints, Vierendeel action (for frames) by shear action (shear walls and plate action in floors)

Structural design

Good design is invisible for several reasons. People generally see only the finished product of the design process and a certain expertise is needed to infer the design effort that went into creating it. People also tend to notice and complain about bad design far more than they notice or praise good design. Furthermore, it is seldom possible to associate designs with individuals: engineering design is the result of collaboration between many members of a design team. Designs may not even have their origins with the current design team since much design is cumulative – once developed, ideas can be freely used by others and improved upon. The humble I-beam, for instance, is a brilliant piece of engineering design which enables buildings to be built using a fraction of the material which would otherwise be needed. Its development, and that of a thousand other structural devices, represents the cumulative effort and experience of many thousands of skilful

engineers stretching back over many decades, even centuries.

It is also important to distinguish between two approaches to structural design representing different attitudes of mind. One way is to design structures by making imaginative use of existing bodies of engineering knowledge and relatively tried-and-tested structural solutions. The results, needless to say, are not likely to be highly innovative but may nevertheless suit a particular building project. Much architecture follows the same approach.

But many designers – both engineers and architects – believe that the best way to achieve good buildings is to go back to first principles and create designs by a combination of inspiration and logic. While architects are usually educated to take this approach, even to the extent of challenging a project brief by questioning the need for a building at all, it is not common in the formation of engineering students. Yet it is only in a climate where precedent and established practice are challenged and building design briefs do not continue to direct designers along well-trodden paths, that genuine innovation can be achieved. Then engineers can be at their most creative and achieve what, with hindsight, is called progress. Although this approach requires and stimulates skills that projects using standard design solutions seldom challenge, it also stems from an attitude of mind in the engineer – when asked how it happened that he was continuously asked to work on interesting projects, Peter Rice replied simply that many of them had not been very interesting when he was first approached.

The art of design, like many skills such as riding a bike or swimming, is learnt mainly by doing, not from reading descriptions of how it is done. Nevertheless, there can be benefit in trying to articulate what one is doing, for instance, by telling someone else. And when doing this, it is probably always the speaker who benefits more than the listener. Articulating what one is doing is a valuable way of raising one's own self awareness, and in this lies the road to improvement and the building of self esteem. In this light, it is interesting to wonder why architects ten to talk about their design process more than structural engineers. The diagram (right) shows how one engineer (Frank Newby) has expressed his view of the engineering design process.

Choosing and developing a structural concept for a particular purpose is a highly creative process. For an architect the form of the structure is constrained only by its function, the site and his or her vision. For structural engineers the form is also constrained by how they intend and expect it will work as a structure, and by the need to provide a rational argument and calculations to justify this

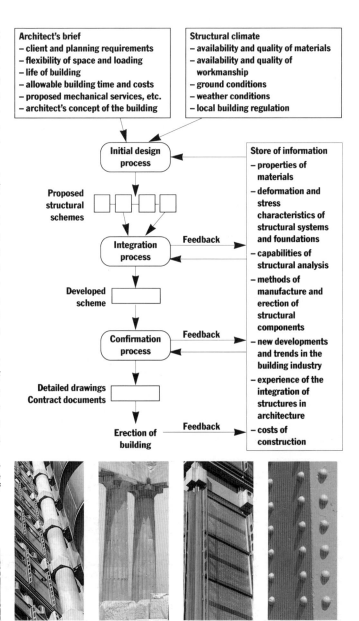

The foundation of engineering is knowledge of material, not, as engineers are so often apt to preach, a knowledge of mathematics.

Alan Harris

expectation before the structure is built. Considerable powers of imagination are needed. To design a structure it is necessary to imagine every conceivable type of failure and then ensure that each one is prevented by deft use of materials. To do this an engineer must be able to apply imaginary loads to structures that do not yet exist and which, even when built, will respond in ways which are too small or slow to see or, in the case of collapse, which he hopes never to see.

The initial choice of a structural scheme is made from a relatively limited number of basic structural forms or actions. These can be developed and adapted and used in combination with each other to create a unique and original whole. By and large, this will arise out of the nature of the loads which need to be carried and how they might be conducted along load paths to available points of support. The engineer's skill lies in choosing an arrangement which manages to satisfy, to varying degrees, many, often incompatible,

constraints. As with architecture and composing music, this skill relies on a mixture of precedent, experience and inspiration. Just how a particular engineer actually conceives a new structure is both highly individual and virtually impossible for anyone else to talk about.

Usually many different schemes will arise and their merits will be compared (qualitatively) with one another and according to how they each meet the functional, architectural, services and foundation requirements. Each scheme must then be tested by imagining how it will behave as a structure under the various loads. It may even be useful to make a string-and-sealing wax model, though more to assist the imagination than to glean any useful structural information. The real testing only begins at the next stage when the leap is made to a quantitative assessment of the structure.

Before the engineer can do any calculations to test a structural idea, a mathematical model of the whole structural system must be created. This model is a combination of three separate and entirely independent primary models – a model of the loads, a model of the material(s) and a model of the structure. The composite model becomes a set of relationships between the various elements of the three primary models – rather like the empty shell of a computer spreadsheet – into which particular values can be entered and certain results calculated. In this way the model can be made to behave and its response studied for a range of stimuli.

It must never be forgotten, however, that the primary models of loads, materials and structure are all idealisations and simplifications of the real world, and the behavioral output of the composite model is merely an infallible consequence of the information contained in the primary models, not of their real-world counterparts. Any predictions made from the output of the composite model about the likely behaviour of the completed structure must be treated with intelligence and care. There is risk associated with this inductive logic. On occasions, an experienced engineer may feel the risk is so great that confirmation of a different kind is advisable. Wind-tunnel tests and the building and testing of prototypes or accurate scale models can give valuable quantitative information about loads, stresses and deflections of structures. These will complement and may confirm the predictions made from purely theoretical 'tests'. Nevertheless, even such physical tests rely on various theories of engineering science for their interpretation and application to the full-size real structure. They, too, must therefore be used with great caution.

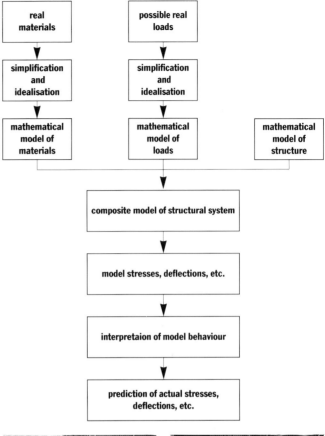

Any project has its cost constraints which must be met. They are a fundamental part of the design challenge, and finding a way to add one's special extra quality while respecting all the other parameters is one of the things which can make the challenge of design interesting and exciting to the engineer.

Peter Rice

Whatever type of structure is conceived, two important goals must be constantly borne in mind. Firstly, the structure must have a form and construction which can be described and specified in minute and precise detail, in order that it can be built. This is not always straightforward for concrete shells and fabric and cable-net structures. The geometrical capabilities of modern three-dimensional CAD software have enabled structures of unprecedented complexity to be built, partly for the simple reason that it is now possible to calculate their shapes and dimensions with greater ease and accuracy.

The computer has also helped structural engineers in meeting the other goal – providing a justification that a structure will perform as expected and be as safe as necessary. The sophisticated geometric computer models of complex structures form an essential part of the composite mathematical model needed to analyse a building's structural behaviour. This increased power to analyse a broader range of structural forms and complexity of structure has brought enormous progress in recent years. Only twenty years ago many of the structures featured in this book – the fabric roofs, cable-net structures and highly redundant moment-resisting frames, to name just three – could not have been built because the mathematics of the geometry and the analysis would have been far too laborious to contemplate, even using the computers of that time. The requirement that a proposed structural form must be able to be justified is now far less restricting than it once was, although a negative consequence of this so-called progress is that it is now easier to produce inelegant and unnecessarily convoluted structures.

In this context it is vital to remember that the performance of a structure is entirely within the control of a good designer. The behaviour of a moment frame, truss or cable-net can be tuned as sensitively as any violin – by adjusting material specification, the type, size and cross-section of members, the position and rigidity of joints, the level of any prestressing, the attachment to any cladding with which it might act compositely, the effect of out-of-plane links such as longitudinal bracing, and so on.

All these technical aspects of the structural engineer's art are tools to be used at the appropriate time. They lie almost dormant in the back of the engineer's mind while he or she gets on with the more public, qualitative parts of the process. In dialogue with non-engineers the talk is of the location of columns, the size, shape and position of voids for services ducts and cables, the depth of floor structures, the location of shear cores, and the movement of different parts of the building relative to each other and the envelope (due to loads, settlement of foundations or thermal effects).

Each of these facets of a structure is interrelated, and the structural engineer is the person who understands their relationship. Take, for instance, the factors which affect the column grid in a building. The loads carried by individual columns need to be matched to the type and cost of different foundations, and these, in turn, depend on the load-carrying capacity of the soil. The column loads depend on the floor loading and the spans between columns which, in turn, affect the depth and spacing of the floor beams and, hence, the space for services, the height of the building and the cost of the cladding. In addition to these structural issues, there is also the influence of the various non-structural grids – the building envelope, the services distribution, furniture, room and corridor layout, basement car parks, and so on.

The advice given by an engineer concerning some area of his

between the rise of an arch and its stability and outward thrust. In a way which is half visual, half feeling, an engineer can imagine all the different consequences of changing column spacing, floor structure, a material, or the relative dimensions of members. The impression is of an imaginary object that is almost alive, much in the way that drivers of steam trains and old cars feel that their machines have their own character and behaviour. Rudyard Kipling wrote a wonderful story, 'The Ship That Found Herself' (not himself, note!), in which he brings alive the structure and engines of a transatlantic ship as they tell their experiences during a stormy voyage. It should be compulsory reading for every engineering degree.

These, then, are the essential aspects of the art of structural engineering design. Put another way, the structural engineer is someone who can make something with a tonne of material that 'any damn fool' can make with ten; someone who can make at full scale what anyone can make at a scale of 1:100 or 1:10; someone who can make for £100 what anyone can make for £1000. The Institution of Structural Engineers expresses the same idea rather more eloquently: 'structural engineering is the science of designing and making, with economy and elegance, buildings, bridges, frameworks, and other similar structures so that they can safely resist the forces to which they may be subjected.'

Much of this type of engineering knowledge cannot be written down and cannot be learnt quickly; it has to be built up gradually and through direct personal experience. It is small wonder that it takes many years to establish creative confident engineering teams

     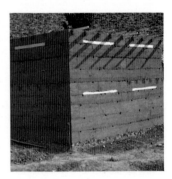

knowledge and skill might sometimes seem conveniently short and simple: 'Choose the form of a truss such that long members act in tension and short ones in compression'; or, 'For an efficient structure use tension in preference to compression, and either in preference to bending.' However, such simple rules are riddled with caveats (which is why engineers need fear nothing from so-called expert-systems). In the case of the truss, for instance, it depends on what uplift there may be, what restraint there is at the supports, whether you want a member to 'disappear' as the force within it goes from tension to compression, what materials and forms of those materials are available, and how much they cost.

The model of a universal building built up by the human mind is far too subtle to feed into any computer, and the workings of this mental image are far too fast to see. An engineer simply knows – feels – the nature of the relationship between floor span and depth, between the shape of a structural section and its deflection,

whose collective knowledge, skills and experience constitute a sufficient palette from which to conceive, evaluate and build new structures.

Engineer and architect

There often arises the question, 'Who designed that building?' The answer is usually, 'An architect.' Nearly always the truth is that a team of architects and engineers designed it. Yet the popular press and even well-known architectural periodicals consistently omit all mention of structural engineers, despite the occasional polite letter pointing the matter out.

Since the Copyright, Design and Patents Act of 1988, architect and structural engineer are treated equally in law. They each have the moral right – *le droit moral* – as co-author and copyright-owner of the design, to fix their name to a building they have designed. This law also gives both architect and engineer the right to have their name against any published photograph of the building. Furthermore, they also have the right to insist that their work is not subject to 'unjustified modification'. While this will not prevent building owners from making alterations, it does entitle architects and engineers to object to photographs of the altered artefacts being published; and they can have their identification removed from the building if they feel it has been degraded by a later hand.

Despite equality in law, the relationship between structural engineer and architect is not symmetrical. Maybe this is why so much has been written about the relationship. The nature of the responsibility each carries is different. If a building is an architectural failure, reputations and bank accounts may suffer; if it experiences a services failure people get too cold or hot. A structural engineer needs to have the confidence to sign a piece of paper saying 'this building will stand up safely for a long time'; he needs all the help he can get to achieve this level of confidence.

Perhaps the relationship fascinates so many writers because the modern architect is utterly dependent on the structural engineer. Yet engineers frequently feel equally dependent on the architect, from whom they may, or may not, get their next job.

There is also the question of authorship, and this can be a very sensitive issue. Human relationships occur in threes rather than twos; it is client, architect, engineer, not just the last two. And in groups of three, jealousies can arise. For example, architects will clearly want to protect their relationship with the client. Yet, is this reason enough for many architects, even some well-known for their structural architecture, to write and talk about buildings as if

the design team contained no structural engineers? Conversely, one prominent engineer declined the opportunity to be credited as co-designer of a building for fear that his architect collaborators might feel he was trying to steal their glory and so would not want to work with him in the future. Does it all come down to the fact that engineers are numerate and architects are visual? If so, why? The roots to such attitudes and emotions go very deep and it all gets very psychological, very quickly.

Like most team activities, the circumstances and type of undertaking influence the nature of the collaboration. In a major civil engineering project the engineer's contribution is dominant; in a bespoke private residence, the architect is to the fore. In hospitals, sports stadia and theatres the contribution is more evenly shared. Personalities, too, are important. There are as many different types of architect/engineer relationships as there are types of married couple. Likewise, there are no more guidelines for a

successful design collaboration than there are recipes for a successful marriage.

Looking at all this another way, engineers have skills which architects lack, and *vice versa*. A sensible architect would surely want to collaborate on the creation of a building which exhibits evidence of more than the sum of two separate sets of skills. But there is always a difficulty when two people with different skills work together. Anyone who has tried to brief a lawyer will know the problem: 'Why didn't you tell me that before?' 'You didn't ask me?' 'How could I ask you if I didn't know what to ask?' 'You should know more about the law.' 'But that's why I'm employing you.' … and so on.

Some people suggest the solution to the gap and discord between the two professions is for them to study together. Others believe that a separation is essential since the very best architecture results from the interaction of unlike minds and creative tensions. Nevertheless, both groups would probably agree that, for the best results, it is beneficial for each profession to know what might be expected of the other, even if this is ignored. It would also be wise to expose and avoid genuine misunderstandings – all engineers and architects should read Alan Harris's *Architectural Misconceptions of Engineering*. Many engineers' lives are made miserable by architects who do not realise the consequences of some of their choices and decisions, or are not even aware that they ought to consider the consequences. Conversely, it is not uncommon for engineers to feel that they are seldom challenged enough by architects, being asked merely to make a building work structurally after most of

Where structure is a major consideration, the engineer should be a partner in evolving the design, so that the proper integration of structure and architecture can be achieved. It is of course his job to assist the architect to realise his architectural conception, and he must accept his role as an assistant. But he should be a useful assistant, and that means that he must understand and sympathise with the aims of the architect, so that he, in his own intuitive thinking, can arrive at proposals which will further the architect's wishes – just as a pianist in his own right should not deem it beneath his dignity to act as an accompanist, as long as he is not asked to play with one finger.

Ove Arup

the design is complete. Although this is one of their vital skills, engineers have many others, including the ability to:

- bring experience from other projects (an engineer will work on many more projects than an architect);
- suggest appropriate structural forms;
- imagine the likely behaviour of a structure that does not yet exist;
- think both qualitatively and quantitatively about loads, materials and structures and switch between both modes of thought;
- have a feel for the properties and behaviour of materials;
- devise a design procedure for a type of structure that has never before been designed or built;
- build scale models to test structural ideas and behaviour and interpret, for use at full size, the results

obtained from a scale model;

- choose appropriate performance criteria against which a structure can be assessed, and limits which it must not transgress;
- understand the implications for other professionals (concerning cost, services, durability, fire resistance, etc.) of the building structure, and *vice versa*;
- assess the buildability of a proposed design and suggest how it can be improved;
- know when the process of structural design has been completed in a satisfactory manner;
- fall back on 'engineering judgement' when all else fails.

The role of both engineers and architects is currently under threat. Some of their work is being taken over by others – quantity surveyors, project managers, design-and-build firms and specialist contractors. Part of the reason for this is that architects and engineers have become too specialised and others have begun, more and more, to manage projects, deal with clients, estimate and control costs, and design for production. On the other hand, they have perhaps done too little to make known the full range of their skills and their place in the process of designing and making a building. One reason why competitive fee tendering has had such a savage effect on both professions is that clients have been unable to understand what it is that engineers and architects contribute that they cannot get, for instance, from a design-and-build firm or a con-

offering needs to be marketed far more effectively than has been necessary in the past. This means articulating the design process and getting people to understand how difficult and time consuming it can be; in short, overcoming the inherent invisibility of what is largely an intellectual process.

Structure and aesthetics

I start from the premise that to be a good structural engineer it is essential to be able to discriminate between good and bad examples of structural engineering. Concern with aesthetics should be addressing what constitutes good and bad design and what it is to be a good structural engineer.

This approach to aesthetics – the study of excellence in an area of creative human activity – is far broader than that of the classical Greek philosophers who studied only what can be directly perceived by the five senses. Nowadays we can no longer keep separate the stimuli from the senses and their interpretation in our minds. The aesthetics of structure go far deeper than how something looks – much depends on who is doing the looking.

The outcome of considering the aesthetics of structure should not be a precise set of rules for creating a good structure. Rather, it should be a better-developed ability to discriminate between good and bad engineering, and a stronger sense that good engineering design matters and can bring a wealth of benefits to building owners, architects and architecture – and to engineers themselves, both personally and collectively as a profession.

The underlying principles of aesthetics can apply equally well to

What happens when one works with different architects is that each architect's attitudes and opinions become part of the problem being solved. And provided one can introduce – as one almost invariably can – an element of engineering exploration either in the nature of materials, or structure, or light, or some other physical phenomenon, no loss of identity or independence need be implied for the engineer.

Peter Rice

Artistic quality or 'delight' can be compared to a coy maiden who will shrink from direct pursuit but pretend to ignore her and get on with your work and she may come running after you. My advice to engineers is to be good engineers first of all.

Ove Arup

tractor. The result, at the time of writing, is that engineers and architects are working long hours. At a time when designers are being urged to take on more and more – energy conservation, green issues, production engineering matters, maintainability – they are being given less time and money to do so.

The consequences are inevitable: if key structural issues are not dealt with early in a project they will need to be done later, and will cost more. The following story is true. On a project which needed a large and complex façade structure, bids were accepted for the cladding and the building structure. Only later did the cladding contractor realise the complexity of the structural issues involved and the client had to employ a second firm of structural engineers, at more expense, to resolve matters. As more examples come to light, perhaps more clients will realise that you only get what you pay for, and the earlier in the project you do it, the cheaper it is.

The lesson for all building designers is clear – the service they are

any work – functional objects such as a tin-opener, 'useless' objects such as paintings, or objects lying somewhere in between, such as an attractive table lamp or a roof structure. Discussion focuses on the various criteria according to which the work might be judged, and the relative importance of these criteria.

Exactly who is offering their views on a work of art is significant. A modern engineer looking at a Gothic cathedral (and its load paths, equilibrium of thrusts, wind bracing, etc.) is seeing a different building from an architect, sculptor or, indeed, a medieval master mason. Perceiving or looking at a structure, either as engineer, architect or sculptor, depends on a knowledge of cultural context and precedent as well as on education and skills of interpretation.

Most of us could quickly list the qualities of a good tin-opener; it would be more challenging to do the same for a painting, or roof structure. Discerning quality in a work of art is often wrapped up in the activity of criticism. The quality of a Rembrandt, a Wren church, or a Rover car arises, in part, from what people say about it, who is saying it, how they make their case for its excellence, and how successful they are at persuading others of their view. It is thus vital to the existence and success of any creative art that there is regular debate – not only so that existing works may be evaluated, but also so that a culture of excellence and quality surrounding that particular art can develop.

An immediate outcome for someone considering the aesthetics of their art will be an improved ability to identify appropriate criteria for judging excellence, to formulate powerful arguments using good rhetoric as to why a particular work is a good one and to criticise an existing work, perhaps even one of their own design or making. In the longer term, the outcome will be better designs and artefacts.

Whatever the reason, it is a fact that there is very much more debate about the aesthetics of architecture than of structural engineering. And yet good engineers do have a well-developed sense of excellence in their art. There are perhaps good psychological reasons why the education and training of engineers does not generally involve the 'crits' so beloved of architecture schools. Engineers are generally brought up on a diet of correct (or incorrect) answers to specified problems – not much room there for debate. Even in open-ended projects there often tends to be an underlying idea that proposals are either right or wrong, rather than having different good and bad points.

A work of art communicates with whoever is experiencing it. Most creators of works of art intend to communicate something,

ture. It will reflect the cultural and engineering climate in which it was conceived and realised. It may communicate some eternal truths or laws of nature: truths about equilibrium and statics, about the nature of structure, or about the mechanical properties of materials. A structure will tell us something of a culture's manufacturing technologies, of the properties of materials which dictate how they may, or may not, be manufactured. It may convey the full wealth of a material's *aesthetic*, its soul. Above all, it will communicate the skill of the designer and the manufacturer.

Good structures are often praised for their elegance. This may well be a reflection of how they look, but when engineers talk of elegant design they mean rather more. There is the hint of an artefact that makes the job it does look easy. Often you can only read this in a design if you know how hard the job was. Engineers allude to this in their claim that 'if a design looks right, it is right', which sounds arrogant but is seldom meant so. Take, for instance, a problem encountered in many roof structures – joining perhaps a dozen members together at one connection. Some designs make this task look easy; others evoke sympathy for the craftsmen who had to fashion and assemble them, even for the materials, bolts and gusset plates themselves!

Engineering elegance is manifest also in the subtlety of the engineering principles employed. The use of post-tensioning, for instance, might substantially reduce the amount of material needed to make a floor structure, with little cost penalty and the bonus of an additional storey squeezed into a building. By exploiting the ductile strength of steel, a new means of safeguarding

If the structural shape does not correspond to the materials of which it is made there can be no aesthetic satisfaction … Our capacity to develop the aesthetic quality of structural harmony, in terms of different materials and its structural requirements, is as undeveloped in our time as orchestration and counterpoint were in the seventeenth century. The reason is possibly the spiritual divorce of our specialised techniques.

Eduardo Torroja

something from within themselves. People talk of works of art 'speaking for themselves', perhaps on behalf their creators. Engineers talk of 'reading a structure'. But the act of communication only works if we understand the language of communication; and the power and effectiveness of the communication depends on the quality of its rhetoric. All this happens when we look at a structure, and in making a judgement about it we are, in effect, answering the question, 'What does this structure say to me?'

At the level of sensations, we perceive the size, form, mass, scale, texture and colour of a structure; and we tend to interpret these in ways are influenced by our culture – as proportion, simplicity, delicacy, elegance. But, most of all, we react to structures. They evoke eye movement; they elicit exclamations of admiration, or otherwise; they rouse enthusiasms such as the desire to look at or take photographs of them, return for second visits, and so on.

A structure may remind us of something in our history or cul-

against collapse in an earthquake zone might be devised which uses less material and releases valuable space for windows and useful floor area.

Materials might be used elegantly in combination to derive benefit from different properties. The strength in tension of glass fibre, and the mass, strength in compression and low cost of cement can be combined in glass-reinforced cement to give a material capable of high resistance to bending and intricate mouldability. By welding shear studs to a steel column and encasing the whole in concrete, the two materials achieve composite action, combining the benefits of steel's strength, stiffness and ease of connection, with the compressive strength, mass, mouldability and fire resistance of concrete.

The structural engineer is constantly seeking, and finding, ever more elegant ways of manufacturing buildings and their components – using standard products to create bespoke designs; devising a structural system which can be made up in factory conditions as a kit of parts for rapid erection on site; using ferrocemento moulds as permanent formwork for a concrete floor to give an exceptional finish to the soffit.

Another aspect of a structure's elegance is the way in which it can simultaneously achieve many functions with economy of components, material and cost. A particularly rich field is that of the interaction between structures and building services. A range of strategies is available, each of which can have its own elegance.

The designers might opt for total separation or zoning. With this method the likelihood of interference is minimised and later changes to the services, and even to the structure, are made easy. Alternatively, certain agreed spaces may be shared, perhaps by using natural voids, such as space between floor beams or holes in castellated beams and roof trusses. A further stage of integration is the planned interpenetration of services runs and structural elements such as dedicated holes and voids made especially for services. A much more efficient use of overall volume can thus be achieved, but with the penalty of the additional effort needed to achieve the co-ordination, and inflexibility in the future.

Finally there is the elegance of total integration achieved when structural components act as parts of the building services systems:
- a concrete plank may contain precast holes that serve as air ducts;
- beams or a floor structure may form the walls of an air duct;
- the thermal inertia of a structural element may be

ture. A complete list would, of course, verge on the tedious since it would need to include the visual arts and architecture as well as highly practical matters such as durability, serviceability and economy. The following is my list of some of the criteria I use when looking at, judging and designing structures; it goes a little further than 'firmness, commodity and delight'. Readers will have, or may develop, their own.
- the skill and clarity with which structural actions, such as tension, compression, bending and shell action, are used and expressed (or hidden);
- elegance and simplicity in joints, structural elements and the structure as a whole;
- structural honesty, or dishonesty when appropriate;
- expression of an appropriate degree of solidity or delicacy;
- economy of material and the appropriateness of a material to its structural function;
- awareness, exploitation and expression of each material's unique aesthetic;
- the choice of a design solution that succeeds in avoiding difficulties rather than surmounting them;
- expression of structural actions in joints;
- juxtaposition of the materials and functions of structural members at joints;
- expression, in a structure's geometry or form, of the imposed loads, structural actions and internal stresses;

I believe we can rethink the way we can use many materials, especially how they are detailed, to express more clearly their engineering nature, and thereby find a new and interesting aesthetic.

Peter Rice

exploited to store heat or coolth;
- structure may absorb or reflect sound, or absorb vibrations of machinery;
- structure may conduct heat or electricity (or not) and allow light to penetrate (or not);
- part of a structure may be filled with water to provide active fire protection.

Likewise, services elements may have a structural function:
- a services core that is also a shear wall;
- a column or beam that also carries away rainwater;
- a duct that also carries loads (for example, those arising from self weight, expansion, wind).

From these examples we can begin to draw up a list of criteria by which we might judge the quality, excellence or elegance of a struc-

- expression of natural geometries such as the circle or catenary;
- selection of a structural form that sensibly anticipates the means by which it can be described (defined) and justified;
- allusion to structural precedents from history, other cultures or nature;
- degree of integration between load-bearing aspects of a structure and non-load-bearing aspects such as cladding and building services;
- expression of the structure's method of construction;
- devising of structural systems capable of repetitive manufacturing processes while retaining stimulating variation and irregularity;
- intelligent anticipation of production engineering problems at the design stage.

Criteria such as these can also help us develop our idea of progress in structural engineering, which is not as obvious as some people would like to believe – it has been observed that modern Codes of Practice are more tedious, no safer and lead to more expensive buildings. Is this progress? People seldom talk of what constitutes progress or how you might evaluate a change and establish whether it would take matters forward or backwards in time. It is a challenging and rewarding exercise to compare two structures built at different times and list all the reasons why one must have been built earlier than the other, or why they could not have been constructed in the other order.

There is surely something to be learnt from the processes of becoming an architect, musician or painter. Criticism and discussion of good and bad, and old and new exemplars of their art play a central part in their education. Surely the formation of structural engineers should include structural criticism, analogous to architectural or music criticism. It would improve their powers of analysis and understanding. It would enhance their ability to explain why a certain structure is well designed and another less well designed, why some deserve their status as classics, why Nervi, Owen Williams and Torroja were great structural engineers. It might also become easier for engineers to articulate to others the nature of structural engineering design as an activity, and thereby reduce the tendency of many to overlook it. Not least, it might also reduce the number of classic structures which are destroyed or molested beyond redemption through ignorance.

By this means, I suspect, engineers' self-esteem and status might

neering education that does little to encourage design, there are many excellent structural engineers. The rest of the book celebrates, by example, their art.

Forty-six buildings have been grouped under seven broad headings: form, structural action, materials, connection, justification, interaction and construction. As an attempt to categorise human creativity, this has its drawbacks. None of the seven categories has a clear boundary; they all overlap. These categories are not objective facts; they are my own and another mind would choose different ones. Projects have been placed in a particular section because they illustrate that aspect of engineering skill well, not because other aspects are absent. Nor does the arrangement of sections imply an order of importance or sequence during a project's development. The categories serve, rather, to give the landscape some features by which to navigate.

A more serious drawback is that in looking at completed projects we miss the most important point about engineering design: the process by which the results were achieved (eating teaches you little of the art of cookery). To get a flavour of the design process at work, an eighth section views the engineering landscape from a different point of view. It looks at just one project and it is the only one in the book that is unbuilt. By following the birth and development of the design as it gradually takes shape, we see something of the interaction and integration of the different skills of engineer and architect.

The selection of buildings generally reflects the enthusiasm of various engineers from a number of well-known design practices

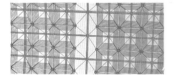  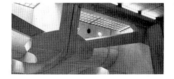 

A technically perfect work can be aesthetically inexpressive but there does not exist, either in the past or the present, a work of architecture which is accepted and recognized as excellent from the aesthetic point of view which is not also excellent from the technical point of view. Good engineering seems to be a necessary though not sufficient condition for good architecture.

Pier Luigi Nervi

begin to rise towards the levels of a century ago; and both clients and architects would better understand the full variety and value of what engineers could contribute to their construction projects, and that it would be worth paying for.

Finally, a personal word on 'archi-structure'. I like it, though only when it is done well. It represents an active interpretation of the idea of structure and can introduce structure into its cultural context. An excellent structural connection, floor slab or roof truss is just that, and I would be the first to agree that they are likely to be a bit dry and listless. But they can be given vitality and character by putting them on show and letting them convey something of their function, something of the human skill behind their conception, their realisation, their crafting, something of the eternal truths of form, structure and material.

All this is generally felt to be the preserve of the architect; not so – it is also the aim of the best engineers. Despite a system of engi-

and the publicity certain people and projects have received in the engineering and architectural press. A project also had to appeal to my eye and engineering sensibility.

Much excellent engineering has been excluded for reasons of space or to avoid repetition. Some aspects of structural design are covered all too briefly, especially the interaction of other design considerations with the building structure: the existing structure in refurbishment work, the building services, the building envelope, energy conservation, soil-structure interaction, and so on.

The accounts of the various buildings help to explain that there are certain decisions about the design of buildings that only structural engineers can make, albeit in collaboration with the rest of the design team. But essentially, the projects serve to bring alive and celebrate the art of the structural engineer and show how different engineers and architects respond to the challenge and exploit the opportunities, when integrating structure into architecture.

Structural action

The structure of a building acts as an armature to enclose the internal space. It must also provide an efficient network of continuous load paths for all likely combinations of wind and gravity loads. At every stage along each load path, a structural element conducts the loads by means of one structural action or another (compression, tension, shear, bending) or in combination with one another (a tied arch, stiffened arch or catenary, prestressed beam, and so on).

To choose a structural action is to impose one type of structural behaviour rather than another. To put three hinges in an arch rather than two, is to do more than make it easier to build. It alters the entire pattern of loads through the structure, the requirement for stiffness, the nature and size of the reactions in the foundations, and the response to thermal loads, let alone the ease of structural analysis. The art of choosing comes from experience – of how and when the enormous range of influences should tip the balance one way rather than another.

Most building structures are frameworks of beams and columns, stable walls and floor plates, carrying their loads in bending or compression, and stiffened and joined to create three-dimensional continuity.

Occasionally, however, a structure will evolve in which, by virtue of its form, significant bending stresses are confined to particular regions (or are insignificant). Loads can then be carried either in pure compression (as an arch), or in tension (as a tie or catenary) or in a combination of direct forces and shears (as a shell). Alternatively, various compression and tension elements – struts, rods, cables, membranes – may be combined to create a space-frame or fabric structure. On such occasions it is difficult not to see the purity of structural action and the very essence of structure expressed in both the elements and the whole.

The purity of structures is generally compromised by the variety of different loads they must endure and the multiplicity of functions that are demanded of a building's structure. The art in selecting structure is in recognising how and when the designer can impose his wishes with a minimum of compromise. Yet, compared with nature, we humans are still in our infancy when it comes to mastering the combination of structural actions. A single orchid flower probably contains more variety and subtlety of structural actions than the most remarkable building; and natural structures have a factor of safety of very nearly one.

There is no method that enables us automatically to discover the most adequate structural type to fit a specific problem, as it is faced by the designer. The achievement of the final solution is largely a matter of habit, intuition, imagination, common sense and personal attitude. Only the accumulation of experience can shorten the necessary labour or trial and error involved in the selection of one among the different possible alternatives.

Eduardo Torroja

The Sainsbury Building

Worcester College, Oxford

1982

Structural engineer **Buro Happold**

Architect **MacCormac . Jamieson . Prichard**

Client **Worcester College, Oxford**

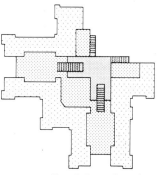

From first appearances this building would seem to be of conventional domestic construction. In fact, the design of both its internal environment and its structure is much more complex and each is intimately integrated with the other.

The building form and structure arose out of a wish to develop a highly energy-efficient building and the architect's idea of grouping a number of student study-bedrooms around a shared kitchen, living room and bathroom. This group of rooms is repeated and stepped back in each of the building's three storeys to create terraces overlooking the lake and college playing field. The layout of the spaces within the building led to an environmental hierarchy, as described below, with the warmest space insulated from the outside by the two cooler spaces in order to minimise temperature differences across walls:

- semi-public corridors: maintained at a low temperature in winter (people are assumed to be wearing outdoor clothes);

- private internal corridors linking study-bedrooms, kitchen, living rooms and bathrooms: maintained at normal room temperature (around 18°C);

- student rooms (a large proportion of the building area), some of which are used only to sleep in, some have near constant occupation, and others irregular use patterns through the day: maintained at 13°C but boostable by the room's occupant.

The energy needed to achieve this environmental performance was minimised by using carefully-chosen structural materials. The walls of the internal, constant-temperature spaces are built of concrete and blockwork with a high thermal inertia and heat capacity. The walls between student bedrooms are of dense concrete blockwork to give good acoustic insulation, while their external walls are of brick and lightweight cavity-wall construction. Both walls and ceilings are lined in a relatively lightweight plasterboard, backed with insulation, to allow the room to warm up quickly when the heating is boosted by its occupant.

These environmental influences had a direct bearing on the design of the load-bearing structure which comprises reinforced-concrete floors supported by

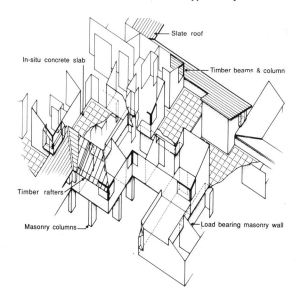

- Slate roof
- In-situ concrete slab
- Timber beams & column
- Timber rafters
- Masonry columns
- Load bearing masonry wall

masonry walls and piers, a type of construction in which dead loads dominate the relatively small live loads. The stepping back of the groups of rooms at each level meant that the load-bearing walls did not necessarily line up from floor to floor as in a normal load-bearing masonry building, and it was no small challenge to ensure satisfactory load paths through the full height of the building.

Where one wall crosses another at right angles there is a concentration of the flow lines of compressive stress, both at the base of the upper wall and the top of the lower wall. A potentially damaging consequence of this is the creation of tension forces in the masonry perpendicular to the lines of compression. The designers needed to ensure that these would not be large enough to cause cracking. This was achieved by incorporating horizontal reinforcement in the walls and introducing joints and articulations to encourage movement rather than a build-up of stresses.

Where a load-bearing wall rests on thin-reinforced-concrete slab, a different problem might arise resulting from the difference in stiffness between the wall and the slab. A typical deflection of a slab designed to carry the imposed loads safely might be around 10 mm. The wall above, however, acts as a very deep and stiff beam in its own right and would deflect much less than 10 mm. (Alternatively, the wall could be thought of as arching between the two supporting walls.) Such an incompatibility of deflections would effectively leave the centre part of the wall unsupported by the slab. Depending on the relative structural properties of the wall and slab, two extreme outcomes might arise: if the blockwork and mortar were strong enough the wall would act as a deep beam and its weight would be carried by the walls beneath rather than the concrete slab; if, however, the masonry were weak in tension, the wall would arch between its supports (with the load path taking the stiffest route to the foundations) and horizontal cracks would form in the centre part of the wall which would then drop onto the slab. Both of these undesirable consequences were avoided by ensuring that the concrete slabs were stiffened sufficiently by using downstand beams or additional reinforcement to keep

stresses in the mortar below its strength in tension and shear.

The pattern of stress flow through the structure of this building is further complicated by the fact that it changes over time. The walls do not acquire their full stiffness immediatelyn: the mortar becomes stiffer as its chemical reactions continue towards their equilibrium state. As they gradually become stiffer, the walls attract a greater share of the loads. Meanwhile, the concrete in the floor slabs is prone to creep and, in so relaxing, the slabs shed load to the stiffer load path through the walls.

The complexity of all these structural matters was resolved by two means, one hi-tech, the other, low-tech. A sophisticated, finite-element computer model of the structure was built to enable the effects of the various interrelated and time-dependent factors to be investigated thoroughly. This was able to provide the engineers with the justification of a structural system which would have been far too complex to handle economically using traditional masonry design procedures.

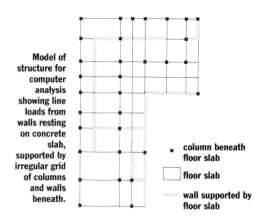

Model of structure for computer analysis showing line loads from walls resting on concrete slab, supported by irregular grid of columns and walls beneath.

■ column beneath floor slab

□ floor slab

⋯ wall supported by floor slab

The 'low-tech' contribution was to use a traditional lime mortar in the masonry. Although this has a lower strength than modern mortars, it is not brittle, and creeps slowly in response to applied loads. It is thus able to assist with the changing load paths and redistribution of loads over time. This property of lime mortar might well be heeded by those who believe that movement joints every few metres are a necessary attribute of modern brickwork – there are many hundreds of miles of pre-1900 walls without a joint to be seen.

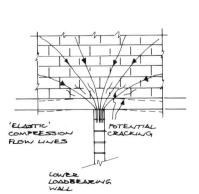

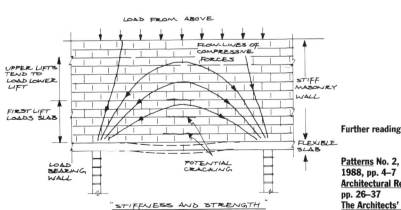

Further reading

Patterns No. 2, Buro Happold, April 1988, pp. 4–7
Architectural Review, September 1983, pp. 26–37
The Architects' Journal, 7 September 1983, pp. 55–76

Bishopstoke Infants School

1989

Structural engineer   **Buro Happold**

Architect   **Hampshire County Council Architects**

Client   **Hampshire County Council**

All buildings need to provide a path load to carry wind loads from the walls or façade down to the foundations. In a rectangular multi-storey building the usual route is horizontally through the floor plates and vertically down the shear core around the services risers, stairs or lift shafts. In a circular, open-plan, low-rise building with a prominent roof, the best route is not quite so obvious.

The plan for this infants school was conceived as a series of class- and activity-rooms radiating off a central communal area. A series of radial shear walls might have seemed a suitable solution but this would have led to a monotonous layout with all-round views out of the building. There would also remain the possibility of the building spiralling into the ground with the walls collapsing like a circle of dominoes.

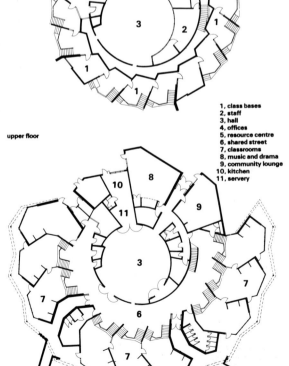

upper floor

ground floor (scale approx 1:500)

1, class bases
2, staff
3, hall
4, offices
5, resource centre
6, shared street
7, classrooms
8, music and drama
9, community lounge
10, kitchen
11, servery

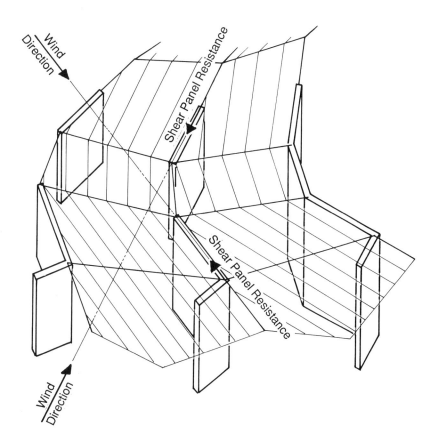

By folding the radial walls they are given a useful, structural cross-section in plan which resists the spiralling collapse as well as the direct wind loads. The result is a highly individual interior made intimate by good visual contact within the building and only occasional views from the central area into the outside world.

However, the wind does not act directly on the shear walls; the façade and conical roof, on which the wind does act, need to be connected to the shear walls, and there needs to be a means of linking the separate walls to distribute the loads between them. This link is provided in two ways. Beneath the exposed surface of the flatter portion of the roof is a layer of overlapping sheets of plywood. These act together as a horizontal shear plate, providing a load path from the external walls to the shear walls and linking the shear walls at their upper ends. Within the building the concrete floor of the upper storey provides a further link between the shear walls at their mid-height.

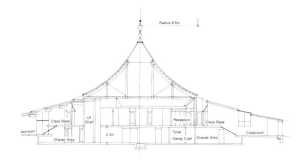

Further reading

<u>Architectural Review</u>, November 1990, pp. 43–48
<u>Patterns</u> No. 8, Buro Happold, 1991, pp. 6–9

Lisson Gallery

London 1991

Structural engineer <u>**Price & Myers**</u>

Architect <u>**Tony Fretton**</u>

Client <u>**The Lisson Gallery**</u>

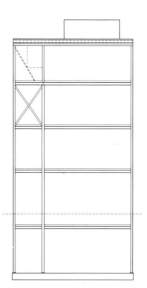

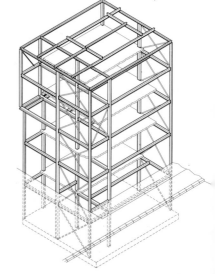

While all buildings need bracing to carry lateral loads, it is often a relatively easy matter to incorporate the necessary structure to provide an uninterrupted load path from, for instance, wind loads impinging on the top storey, down through every storey to the foundations. The loads are usually carried first horizontally through the floor plate and then downwards through cross-bracing or a shear wall incorporated within the external walls or internal cores containing services, lifts or stairs.

The street façade in the architect's scheme for the Lisson Gallery called for three windows of virtually full width and floors of a minimum depth. The rear façade likewise had a large number of windows. Internally, the gallery spaces include very few walls and no single staircase climbs the full height of the building. There were thus very few areas of vertical surface to act as shear walls. (In fact, in the final scheme, not all the full-width windows were incorporated.)

A solution was finally found by using what little wall was available for shear bracing – one bay on the second floor at the front and most of a bay on the top floor at the rear. This bracing was augmented by ensuring that the connections in the steel structure would carry bending moments and act as a Vierendeel frame. The increased moment-carrying capacity was achieved by making use of every last millimetre (literally) of space between the windows and the frame and by introducing steel gussets into the joints within the depth of the floor screed. The result is a building

which appears to have hardly enough structure to support itself, let alone the heavy sculptures within, and is even more breathtaking when one mentally removes the adjacent buildings.

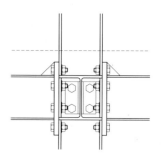

Further reading

<u>Architectural Review</u>, October 1992, pp. 69–72
<u>Architecture Today</u>, January 1992, pp. 20–25

Tsim Sha Tsui Cultural Centre

Hong Kong 1988

Structural engineer **Buro Happold**

Architect **Architectural Services Department, Hong Kong Government**

Client **Building Development Department, Hong Kong Government**

A single roof of some 10,000 square metres was needed to cover three auditoriums (totalling 4300 seats), conference facilities and an enormous foyer in this cultural centre; and it was the architects' strong wish that the space beneath should be column-free. This remarkable achievement was made possible by the use of a suspended cable-net roof structure. However, in its pure form, such a structure has several inherent and serious disadvantages.

The shape of the roof gives rise to substantial and non-uniform uplift forces on the roof in typhoon conditions. Being so light, these loads would cause

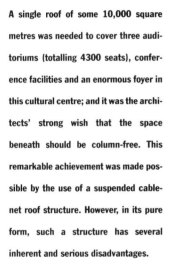

large local deflections since the net has virtually no out-of-plane stiffness. There would also be the possibility of wind-induced oscillations. Over the full span of about 110 metres there would also be significant vertical movements due to both thermal expansion of the cables and changing vertical loads on the roof caused by even light winds. In strong winds (typhoons up to 250 km per hour) the upward suction on the roof would be several times greater than its own weight. There would also be a geometric problem - the architects' profile for the roof did not correspond to the shape which a net would take up when hanging

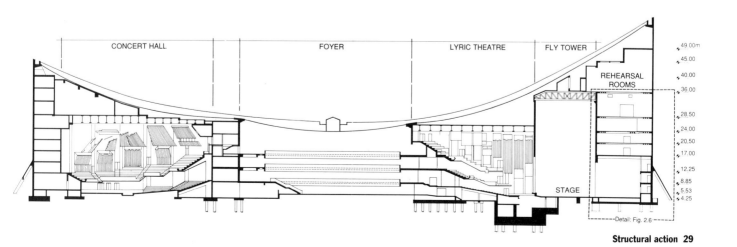

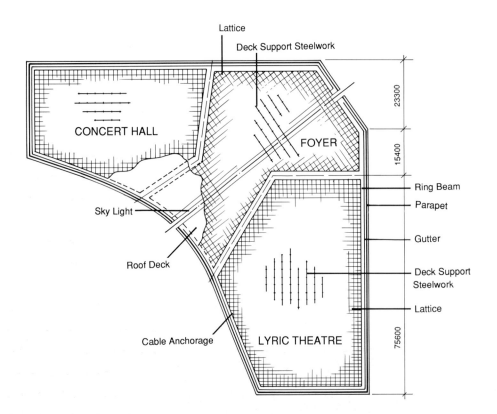

The ability of the stiffened cables to carry compression forces helped overcome the major disadvantage of this type of tension structure: namely, the uplift (greater than the roof's self-weight) caused by winds. It was Robert Hooke who first observed (in 1675) that a hanging chain, when inverted, gives the best form for an arch subject to the same loads. In this case the hanging cable net, when subjected to inverted loads, can act as a lattice shell dome with the cables, stiffened by the concrete, acting in compression. As with normal loading, the concrete beams encasing the cables give the compression lattice sufficient out-of-plane stiffness to resist asymmetrical wind loadings in bending.

The development of a stiffened cable net, able to resist the variety and size of wind loads in a typhoon region, avoided the need for internal columns to support the roof. However, the architects' wish for a totally column-free space at foyer level could only be realised by creating a variety of ingenious, extremely three-dimensional and completely hidden load paths to carry other vertical loads down to the ground.

At ground-floor level there are, in fact, a few internal walls and the engineers were able to take advantage of some of these and give them the support necessary to cantilever out into the foyer spaces. In other parts of the building, interior walls act as very deep beams – some as deep as 17 metres – spanning between the small sections of wall that reach down to foyer level. The interme-

freely. It took considerable ingenuity to overcome the various disadvantages presented by a pure cable net.

Two intermediate ring-beams divide the roof into three smaller areas. This cut spans to about 40 metres and reduced the amount of stiffening required. It also allowed the roof profile to match more closely the shape wanted by the architect, but not closely enough. The final external shape of the roof was formed by fixing cladding to purlins on tubular-steel rafters. These in turn were positioned at the appropriate height above the concrete-covered cable net by a grid of columns of different lengths.

Of the several ways of reducing deflections in a tension structure, perhaps the simplest is to change the ratio of live to dead loads by making the struc-

ture heavier. This turned out to be too expensive: the larger dead load would have needed much larger cables and stronger supports at the perimeter of the net. Prestressing could not be used either, since this can only be used in a doubly-curved surface.

The method finally chosen for stiffening the cable net was to embed each cable in a reinforced-concrete beam. This would seem at first to destroy the elegance of a delicate, lightweight net of thin, steel cables. However, not only does the concrete add to the dead weight of the suspended mesh, but also the beams can be reinforced to give them substantial stiffness in their own right. In addition, unlike the cables, the beams are able to withstand compression forces and act as struts.

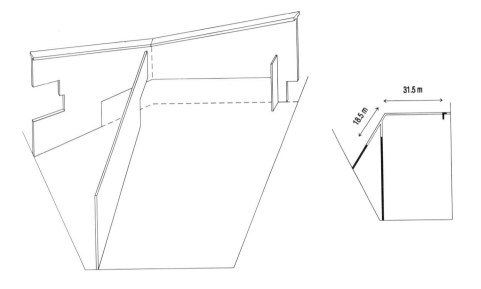

diate ring-beams of the cable-net roof are supported in this manner. One interior wall acts as a T-section beam 6 metres deep with a span of some 31.5 metres. The inner end of the beam is itself supported by two other interior walls which cantilever out from their supports at ground level; one of these cantilevers some 18.5 metres and has a structural depth decreasing from 9 to 4 metres.

Elsewhere in the building other structural devices are employed. The concrete floor slabs of the cantilevered galleries are stiffened and partly supported by their deep edge-walls. A bridge section of the first-floor gallery is suspended by steel hangers from a deep-cantilevered floor slab above. The main staircases rising from foyer to first-floor level act not only as beams but also, in conjunction with the gallery and foyer floors, as a tied arch spanning over 20 metres. These and many other examples throughout this building illustrate how the engineer can exploit various architectural features for structural ends – the very converse of what is found in the work of architects with a different attitude to structure.

Further reading

Proceedings of the Institution of Civil Engineers, Vol. 88, Part 1, 1990, pp. 753–813
Patterns No. 9, Buro Happold, October 1991

Don Valley Stadium

Sheffield 1990

Structural engineer   Anthony Hunt, Steve Morley
<u>YRM-Anthony Hunt Associates</u>
<u>(Sheffield)</u>

Architect   <u>Design and Building Services,</u>
Sheffield City Council

Client   <u>Sheffield for Health</u>

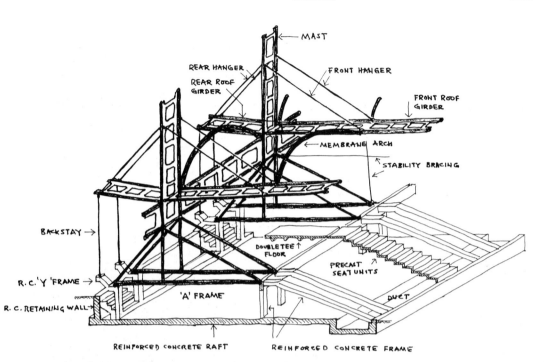

MAST

FRONT HANGER

REAR HANGER

REAR ROOF GIRDER

FRONT ROOF GIRDER

MEMBRANE ARCH

STABILITY BRACING

BACKSTAY

R.C.'Y'FRAME

R.C. RETAINING WALL

DOUBLE TEE FLOOR

'A' FRAME

PRECAST SEAT UNITS

DUCT

REINFORCED CONCRETE RAFT

REINFORCED CONCRETE FRAME

alternative shapes were considered by architect and engineer and the final choice was a series of saddles between the masts with a conical form at the corners.

With such high stress involved it is imperative that the membrane is cut and sewn in precisely the right shape so that over-stressing and slack areas are avoided entirely. The shape of this type of membrane can be controlled by adjusting the levels of the radial and hoop stresses and the geometry of the boundaries; in particular, the stresses and shape are very sensitive to the diameter of the central hole. First of all, a computer program finds the form that a

A roof over a grandstand gives both architect and engineer the rare opportunity to expose the heart and soul of a building's structure. As an acknowledgement to the heritage of the city and the site (a former steelworks), steel is used in the form of simple cantilevers to support a translucent structural-membrane roof over the 10,000-seat main grandstand. As perceived by the public the roof is a 'simple' tent structure supported by a steel frame. The section of the roof cantilevered over the spectators is kept in balance by the steel cable tying the steel frame down to the back of the stand. At this level the entire structural concept is plain to see.

At a deeper level, the story is more complex – the stresses in the roof membrane are hundreds of times higher than in an ordinary tent and a substantial supporting frame was needed. Also, because wind loads on such a roof are large and varied, some elements of the

supporting structure, which look as though they will only ever carry tensile forces, need on occasions to carry large compression forces.

As the client required the membrane to have a long life in service, a relatively new material was chosen. Teflon-coated woven glass fibre is both durable and strong; it weighs just 1.6 kg/m² and has an ultimate tensile strength of 16 tonnes per metre width. Although 93 per cent opaque, the fabric is noticeably translucent both by day and by night; grey in its early life, it is slowly bleached by sunlight and, being 'non-stick', tends not to attract dirt.

A membrane structure needs be tensioned throughout its surface in order to prevent fluttering in wind or large deflections under wind and snow loads. This is achieved by using a doubly-curved (anticlastic) shape which, unlike its ancestor, the tent, can be highly prestressed (to 0.5 tonnes per metre). A number of

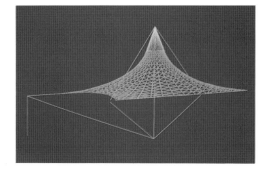

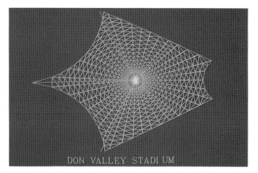

DON VALLEY STADIUM

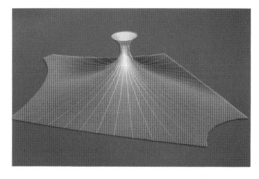

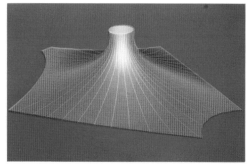

membrane would take up with uniform tension in all directions. This process is the mathematical equivalent of lifting the centre of a flat soap bubble using a circular loop – if the central loop is too small, or lifted too much, the bubble bursts (in computing terms, the iterative calculation does not converge on an equilibrium state). The results can nowadays be represented on a computer screen and a shape which is neither too flat nor with pronounced necking can be selected visually. Having found a suitable shape, the computer model of the form is combined with a model of the material properties of the elastic membrane to generate a new, slightly different equilibrium shape. The distribution of stresses in the membrane is calculated and can also be displayed visually; if these are too high or too low the process can be repeated with new input data. Lastly, a series of patterns is computed to enable panels of the membrane material to be cut and sewn to create the correct final form.

The membrane in the corner cones is prestressed by a three-dimensional system of cables and struts. These, too, needed to be designed using a mathematical model to balance the stresses in the membrane with those in the pre-

stressing structure.

It was noted that the required training facilities, which included an indoor running track, could be located under the main grandstand and so save both building area and cost: but how, then, would the roof mast, seating and concourse be supported. The solution was to reflect, at the rear, the raking beams which support the seating at the front and link them by a horizontal tie at concourse level to form a structurally-efficient tied A-frame. This same clear expression of forces was used in the simple front hanger and backstay arrangement which supports the 26-metre roof cantilevers.

To accommodate the routes from the concourse out onto the seating and to keep the spans reasonable, the engineers suggested twinning the A-frames either side of the access ways. The paired masts and roof cantilevers could then be linked to form Vierendeel girders and give the structure its longitudinal stability. This form of the horizontal cantilevers gives vivid expression to the large tension forces they appear to carry between adjacent membranes. In fact, as can be seen at the corners of the stand, each bay is self-supporting, both to facilitate erection and tensioning of the membranes and to prevent a progressive collapse should one membrane be damaged by tearing or fire.

The 19-metre-long front hangers that support the cantilevers also have to resist substantial compression under wind uplift and are constructed of steel tubes which have good resistance to buckling in all directions. The hangers are joined to the cantilevers by pin-connections to eliminate bending in the members. This would cause them to curve and so reduce the hangers' ability to resist buckling when acting as slender struts in compression.

In such an exposed structure the joints cannot be hidden; particular attention had to be given to this aspect during design to ensure correct functioning and easy assembly – as well as

an elegant appearance which would communicate the material and structural aesthetic of the building. Steel-to-steel interfaces in the pin-joint would suffer from corrosion and soon cease to rotate freely. Plastic shell-bearings around the pins ensure free rotation throughout the life of the structure, and shaped castings carry the forces from the wall of the tubes smoothly into the pinned plates.

The backstay is anchored to the reinforced-concrete frame by an adjustable connection which is easily seen by the public. A concrete Y-frame gives the foundation a feeling of solidity while the strength of the element is provided by the reinforcement embedded inside a simple and sculptured shape.

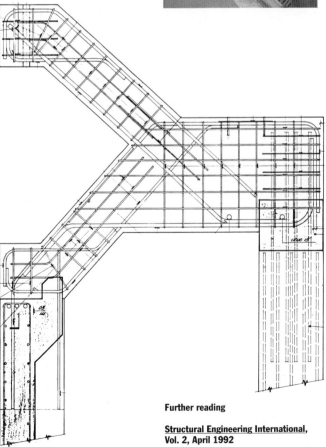

Further reading

<u>Structural Engineering International</u>,
Vol. 2, April 1992

Blue Boar Court

Cambridge 1990

Structural engineer **Phil Cooper**

Harris & Sutherland

Architect **MacCormac Jamieson Prichard & Wright**

Client **Trinity College, Cambridge**

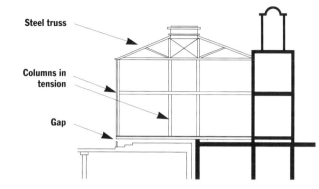

Steel truss

Columns in tension

Gap

Trinity College wished to redevelop an old city-centre hotel site into a fine residential courtyard, gaining some valuable commercial space in the process. On a podium formed by the roof over the existing shops, new and old buildings now form a series of intricate courts linked by bridges, ramps and passages. What is not so obvious is the scarcity of support for these apparently massive, traditional brick and stone buildings. The structural engineer's contribution to design is often discreet -- sometimes, indeed, invisible or deceptive.

Normally the space in which an engineer is free to build is enclosed only by a site boundary. Here the space for development also had to interlock with existing buildings, both above and below. For the architect the design

became a complex three-dimensional puzzle comprising closely-packed rooms arranged around courtyards. For the engineer the challenge was to construct these buildings, some of which were stranded with no obvious means of structural support.

Although the brick façade of the Common Room exactly matches adjacent load-bearing masonry buildings, it is in fact framed in steel and timber. And this is not the only sleight-of-hand; more than half of the Common Room is cantilevered out over Sainsbury's and Heffers Bookshop and is counterbalanced by the large weight of the adjacent tower

and its basement. Although the columns appear, as one might expect, to support the upper floors and roof, it is the roof that supports the floors, and the 'columns', made of steel tube clad in oak, are actually working in tension.

The 140-seat lecture theatre is built on the roof of Sainsbury's supermarket. Settlement and cracking had to be avoided at any price since access to the interior of the busy supermarket was denied totally. Only four columns were available to carry all the loads from the new theatre down through the supermarket to the raft foundation.

The weight of the paving on the original roof was removed and the weight of the new theatre had to be pared to the bone. Indeed, so nearly did the loads carried by the four columns approach the limit that the process became more like that of designing an aircraft – even the weight of an extra layer of plasterboard for acoustic insulation had to be traded against other more essential loads. Although these columns do now carry larger loads than originally, the design engineers were able to provide adequate justification that there was enough reserve capacity to ensure that safety standards for the public shopping areas below would not be compromised.

Further reading

The Architects' Journal,
5 December 1990, pp. 32–43 and
48–49

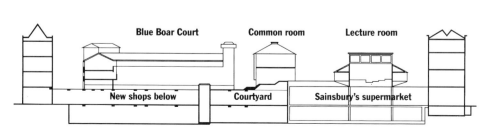

Blue Boar Court   Common room   Lecture room

New shops below   Courtyard   Sainsbury's supermarket

Communications Tower

Barcelona, Spain

1992

Structural engineer Chris Wise

Ove Arup & Partners

Architect Foster Associates

Client Torre de Collserola SA

Engineer and architect worked closely to conceive the Barcelona Communications Tower as a functional and elegant structure. Its three-sided shape on plan, for instance, reflects the functional needs of such a tower: all-round vision, and the minimum number of guys necessary to support a mast. The result of this close collaboration is a structural concept which is so simple and 'obvious' that it is surprising that it has never before been used in a tall tower.

The structure, nearly as high as the Eiffel Tower, comprises a concrete tube for two-thirds of its 288 metres and above this, a steel tube topped, finally, by a crane. Unlike other tall towers, this slender mast is not restrained by a series of stays at regular intervals between bottom and top; nor is it a stiff self-supporting cantilever. The central tube is stiffened by three prestressed trussing systems which work in the same manner as the rigging of a yacht's mast – cables which pass from top to bottom over intermediate outriggers are highly tensioned and put the mast itself into compression. This stiffened tube is kept

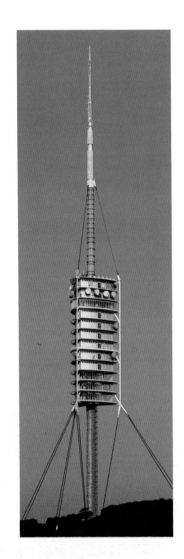

upright by three pairs of guy ropes.

At their lower end the trussing 'wires' are parallel-strand steel cables 320 mm in diameter. At the upper end they are fibre ropes made of Kevlar 49, each comprising seven cables 50 mm in diameter. This material is as strong as steel and half as stiff; and as it does not conduct electricity there is no interference with communication signals.

The outriggers of the trussing system serve also to stiffen the building on plan.

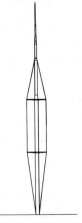

Trussing structure to stiffen column

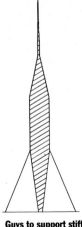

Guys to support stiff column

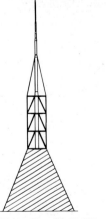

Diagonal bracing to stiffen cantilevered section of tower

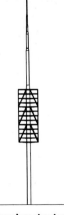

Secondary structure to support floors

Wind impinging on the communication dishes and exposed faces of the equipment floors can impose considerable torsion loads on the tower. The outriggers, which also support the equipment floors, are designed as cantilevers on plan to transmit the torsion loads from the perimeter of the tower to the central, reinforced-concrete core. The tubular cross-section of the core – a constant internal diameter of 3 metres and wall thickness varying from 750 mm at the base to just 300 mm at the top of the truss – is the most efficient type of structure to conduct the torsion loads down to the foundations.

In the vertical plane of the basic truss are three sets of diagonals. These serve two purposes: they stiffen the upper portion of the tower, which effectively acts as a cantilever above the level of the guys; and they carry the weight of the twelve equipment floors and their imposed loads back to the central concrete core. This substantially reduces the forces that the trussing wires have to carry.

The guys that stabilise the tower, being cables, are unable to withstand compression forces, and yet the possibility of the guys going slack when the tower is subject to high wind loads had

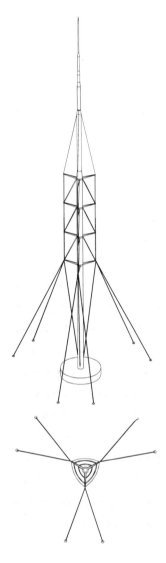

built on flat land, a further subtlety to the design of the guys was needed. Had they all been of the same cross-section, the shorter guys would have been stiffer and thus attracted a disproportionately large share of the total load being carried. The shorter guys were made less stiff to match the elasticity of the longer ones by reducing the number of strands in the steel cable.

Wind loads on such a tall, exposed tower are high – up to 5 kN/m² at the top – and the equipment floors present to the wind about the same area as a 25-storey office block. Wind tunnel tests were done on the tower to investigate both the wind flows over the landscape and the air flow around the equipment floors themselves. These helped to jus-

tify the theoretical assumptions about wind loading and to ensure that small wind eddies would not set the tower or its elements into dangerous oscillation (which caused the collapse of the Tacoma Narrows suspension bridge in 1940). These tests enabled the weight of the tower, and of the equipment floors in particular, to be substantially reduced. It weighs about 2700 tonnes, a third of the weight of an equivalent 7500 square-metre terrestrial office block. The light weight also eased the task of raising the 12-storey block from ground level, where it was built, into its final position 85 metres up the tower.

Further reading

The Structural Engineer, 19 October 1993, pp. 353–358
The Architects' Journal, 17 June 1992, pp. 22–23

to be avoided. By prestressing the guys against the central concrete tube, which is a structural form well able to carry compressive loads, a guy can, effectively, be made to carry a compressive force by having its pretension force reduced.

Rather than the absolute minimum of three guys, six (three splayed pairs) are used. These give a margin of safety as protection against the horrific consequences should one of only three cables be severely damaged; they also provide some additional torsional stiffness to the structure in plan. Since the tower is not

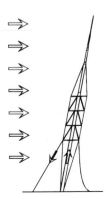

Without prestressing

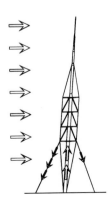

With prestressing

Construction

It is no coincidence that many engineers who have gained reputations as great structural engineers had their roots firmly embedded in contracting and construction firms – Eiffel, Maillart, Hennebique, Torroja, Owen Williams, Samuely, Freyssinet, Nervi, Ove Arup, Jean Prouvé and Candela are just some examples. These men knew their construction materials and manufacturing processes intimately.

It is also often forgotten that our ancestors were able to build as quickly as we can today. The Crystal Palace of 1851 covered 17 acres of Hyde Park (some 70,000 square metres) and some 60 per cent of this was two or three storeys high; it was built, from signing of contract to hand-over, in 26 weeks. More recently, it took the same amount of time to erect the steel frame of the 102-storey Empire State Building.

We live now in a different age. Hardly any structural engineers have spent more than their statutory year on site and so miss the opportunity to build up a first-hand working knowledge of materials and the processes of manufacture, fabrication, production and construction. Yet this has happened in an era when buildings have become more and more complex, the choice of materials and methods used in construction has increased greatly, there are more members of the design team, and all the pressures are to design and build ever more quickly.

There is no easy answer. Since the structural skeleton creates the basis of the architectural form, and provides routes for the services and support for the building envelope and fittings, the structural engineer needs to be sensitive to the requirements of all the other members of the design team. Structural engineers are also the only members of the design team to embrace a good understanding of manufacturing and fabrication processes and possess a feel for the behaviour of materials and structures. A good engineer will be thinking of the way in which the structure, and hence the building, will be constructed even as he is conceiving the forms and connections.

Thus, although modern structural engineers may not have the same quality of construction experience as their predecessors, they should still be the key person to influence the design of a building in order to achieve good co-ordination and integration, and to improve its buildability. It has to be admitted, however, that few structural engineers exploit this position fully, and fewer clients or architects press them for such a contribution. Maybe the threat of design-and-build contracts will change things.

Design ... is nothing else than indicating a sensible way of building. It includes all drawings, specifications, descriptions and detailed instructions about what should be built and how it should be built. Some of these instructions may emanate from the client or the contractor – but they must be absorbed by the designer and made part of the design.

Ove Arup

I think it is absolutely essential that we come into contact with industry again [though], on the whole, the experience is that industry doesn't want us ... I think everybody in industry develops a defence mechanism: the feeling that knowledge is power and that if they somehow let you intervene in their process they will never be able to control it again. We actually have to go out and force our way in; we're not going to be invited in.

Peter Rice

Halley Research Station

No. 4, Brunt Ice Shelf, Antarctica

1983

Structural engineer	Mark Whitby	Timber contractor	Structaply Limited
	Anthony Hunt Associates	Architect	Angus Jamieson Associates
		Client	British Antarctic Survey

Few buildings travel a distance of 6 kilometres during their useful life; even fewer undertake such a journey underground. In just about every way, a building in the Antarctic is different from what we are all used to. In being so isolated it resembles a space station: from the outset it was known that this building would be totally covered by snow in just a few months; the ice shelf, which floats on the sea, is effectively the end of a glacier and moves about 900 metres each year; materials (except snow) would have to be brought in by ship; construction would have to be completed during the period (72 days) when a ship was able to get to the ice shelf, but during that time work could continue 24 hours a day under the midnight sun.

There has been a British Antarctic Survey research station here since 1956 and the three previous buildings have provided the Survey with invaluable experience in how to design for such an environment. The first building was a timber shed with a substantial roof truss and central column to support the snow that would soon accumulate. It was used for 11 years until 14 metres of snow crushed it. The second building was a steel portal frame, which failed in the same manner after seven years when it was 10 metres beneath the surface.

The third building took note of the similarity between the loads it would suffer and those experienced by a tunnel or submerged tube. An Armco corrugated steel tube, of the type often used to form culverts under roads, resting on a timber raft foundation, acted as a protec-

tive cocoon for a non-load-bearing prefabricated timber building. It failed at a depth of 16 metres after 12 years when the bottom of the tube was pushed up by the snow pressures – being a larger radius, the bottom was the weak point in resisting all-round pressure.

Halley 1   Halley 2   Halley 3   Halley 4

Following this failure it was a natural step to consider a circular protective tube for the next research station, Halley 4. In addressing the building's construction, the main challenge was to devise a means whereby its components could be transported and erected easily, and provide adequate structural performance both when newly built and in later life. Immediately after construction it would be at its most vulnerable – a flexible tube resting on a flat surface tends to want to sag and form an oval cross-section; after an Antarctic winter it would be covered by a few metres of snow and would behave as a thin-walled tube.

The design engineer's first step in a project is to develop an adequate understanding of the likely loads on a structure and the properties of the material so that mathematical models can be created to try to predict real structural behaviour. In this case there was little information available, either about loads on buildings buried under snow, or the structural properties of snow itself. The key facts to emerge were that the strength of the snow depended very much on its density and temperature, particularly in the ranges likely to be experienced in the vicinity of the building (450–750 kg/m^3 and between –5 and –18°C).

Structaply worked together with the design engineers to develop a prefabricated timber module that could be assembled, rather in the manner of a Chinese interlocking wooden puzzle, to form a tube which would be resistant

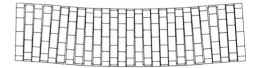

enough to bending to stand alone until covered by snow. The tendency to collapse under its own weight was reduced by excavating a foundation in the snow to support about a quarter of the tube's

Another unanticipated phenomenon further aggravated this problem. Air was able to reach the snow at the sides of the tube and cause it to sublimate. This created small voids and prevented the snow developing its full lateral pressure on the tube which was so essential to the its stability.

The measurements of the building's geometry taken during its occupation will be useful when designing in similar conditions. With hindsight, perhaps the tube should have been slightly oval in the vertical axis and buried more deeply at the beginning. In fact, Halley Research Station No. 5 has a different design philosophy – it resembles a massive, well-insulated Portakabin and is jacked up by about a metre each year on its twenty legs.

circumference (three segments). In addition, snow was heaped and packed up against the walls to give extra support to another segment on each side.

The interlocking segments were held in place during construction by nails, but were designed to be able to articulate to allow the tube to flex under the action of varying loads and differential settlements of the building as it was buried and travelled in the snow towards the open sea.

The accommodation hut sits inside the segmented tube on longitudinal plywood box beams which are located at the points on the tube's cross section which

move least when it deforms into an oval. Initially these beams were fixed to the tube segments to help keep the tube straight. After two years they were disconnected to allow the segments to flex and adapt to the surroundings.

The building survived for ten years until 1992, rather less than fifteen years intended. The need to make the segments easy to assemble left the freestanding building a little too flexible and the tube sagged a little too much during its life before being covered by snow. The result was that the tube was slightly flattened and not able to develop its full strength when acting as a tunnel.

Further reading

Proceedings of 1991 International
Timber Engineering Conference,
London, TRADA, Vol. 2, pp. 109–118

Royal Life
Headquarters Building

Peterborough 1991

Structural engineer **Arup Associates**

Architect **Arup Associates**

Client **Royal Life Holdings Limited**

The first schemes for this new headquarters building incorporated a coffered floor slab and represented the natural evolution of a structure and servicing philosophy that the practice had developed over many years in a wide variety of building types. The site chosen for the building was known to be of weak clay and the coffered structure would have required a large number of piles some 20 metres long. This sub-structure would have consumed a significant proportion of the total building costs and construction time.

Often a client will have in mind a certain cost for a new building well before it has been designed. If the chosen site presents unforseen problems below ground, this may simply mean that a larger proportion of the money will be needed for elaborate foundations and this will have to be found by reducing the proportion spent above ground. Conversely, if an ingenious means can be found to reduce foundation costs, the client might then be able to spend more money on the visible parts and get an altogether higher quality of building.

The site investigation confirmed the existence of the weak clay and revealed an unexpected layer of Cornbrash (a cemented sandstone) covering the entire site. It varied in depth from 3 to 6 metres below ground level, was only about 800 mm thick and cracked in a number of places. There was no possibility that this layer could support the proposed building and the 20-metre piles that would have to be driven through it. Spurred on, perhaps, by

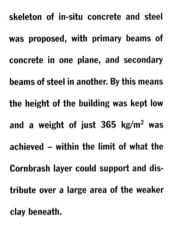

thoughts of the cost of this operation, the structural engineer looked at the problem from the other end: what load <u>could</u> the Cornbrash layer support? The answer was a building with a self weight less than half that of the original scheme – a challenge indeed.

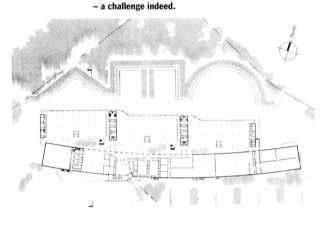

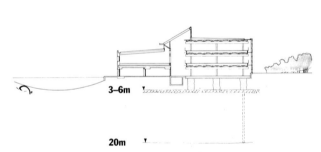

3–6m

20m

One by one different structural ideas were considered which would reduce the original self weight of about 820 kg/m^2 per square metre. By decreasing the size of the grillage of the coffered floor the weight would be reduced to 760 kg/m^2. A composite in-situ/precast scheme was examined: precast troughs where downstands would be exposed, and just strong enough to support the weight of wet concrete when casting the main floor structure. It would weigh about 630 kg/m^2. A flat slab with raised floor was considered: this would reduce the building height and bring the weight to around 600 kg/m^2. Finally a hybrid

skeleton of in-situ concrete and steel was proposed, with primary beams of concrete in one plane, and secondary beams of steel in another. By this means the height of the building was kept low and a weight of just 365 kg/m^2 was achieved – within the limit of what the Cornbrash layer could support and distribute over a large area of the weaker clay beneath.

One key to the success of the hybrid scheme was the decision to link pairs of concrete frames containing the primary beams – by means of small concrete beams in the plane of the steel secondary structure – to form a series of Vierendeel towers. Their resistance to wind loads is augmented by the steel beam and metal decking floor structure which links and acts compositely with the towers to provide longitudinal stability.

The hybrid construction was inherently quick to build – important to a client who wanted to occupy the building as soon as possible. An all-concrete frame and floor could have started on site quickly but would have taken longer to complete; an all-steel frame and metal decking floor would have been quick to construct but the lead time for the structural steelwork would have meant a long delay before work could start on site. The hybrid scheme allowed the frame to begin immediately and be completed during the lead-in time for the steelwork.

As well as being lighter, the hybrid structure itself was also cheaper – about two thirds of the cost of the earliest scheme; and, of course, the greatest saving was in the cost of the (non-visible) structure below ground. Rather than a forest of long and costly piles, the foundations effectively comprise a grid of short concrete pillars. These serve two purposes: they carry the loads from the building directly down to the Cornbrash rock and spread the load from each column foot over an area large enough to prevent the columns from puncturing the thin rock layer. They would also serve to seal any fissures in the rock and protect the crack edges from potentially damaging load concentrations. The cost of these foundations was kept very low by using the clay above the Cornbrash as the formwork for the pillars. Holes were made using the largest available auger (2 metres diameter) to drill down through the clay to the rock. After cleaning out and inspection

these were immediately filled with concrete without even the need to support the sides of the holes.

Despite the constructional logic behind all these ideas, two important aspects of the original architectural scheme were in danger of being lost – a coffered ceiling and exposed concrete of the quality usually achieved by precasting.

The structural engineer was able to deliver the required high-quality finish to the concrete by contributing to the development of a 'structured formwork' system for use on site which incorporated many of the benefits of precasting techniques. A U-shaped trough 4.5 metres long was made by folding a steel plate to produce corner radii three times smaller (just 8 mm) than the usually-quoted minimum. A series of fins was welded to the plate to prevent distortion and the sides supported by external bracing. The bracing structure incorporates the mechanism which allows the sides to be pulled apart to facilitate removing the formwork; it also supports a walkway for use when placing the reinforcement and concrete, thus reducing the need for access scaffolding. The two sides of the mould are joined by a clamp which serves to restrain the sides during pouring and to support the tie-down bolts for the steel secondary beams.

The floor structure allows flexible distribution of services. Longitudinal runs are beneath a raised floor and large transverse service runs are created by the suspended flat ceiling in the short

bays of the concrete Vierendeel towers. This strategy enabled the services to be installed quickly and cheaply and with a minimum of effort: access to all the services voids was easy and no large holes had to be made through structural members. The final development of the ceiling was to incorporate a suspended vault between the secondary beams in the long bays. This controls both light and acoustic to achieve the required degree of intimacy in the office space.

In summary, while the hybrid scheme began 'merely' as a technical device, its adoption and development made a fundamental contribution to the aesthetic and the architecture of the whole building.

All designs change as they develop, and ingenuity is often stretched when major new ideas appear well into a project. It had originally been intended that the façade of the office building would follow the line of the structural frame where the building steps back at the lift and stair cores. As the design of the glazed screen developed it was decided that the façade should sweep in a curve from one block to the next in order to avoid the abruptness of the sudden change of plane and to reinforce the idea of a screen between the building and the surrounding formal landscape. But this

would take the façade some 7 metres away from the frame at two points, at which it would need its own load-bearing structure. Unfortunately, the only steel tube available at such short notice was too small in diameter. Making a virtue out of necessity, the section stiffness of the available tube was increased by welding four pairs of longitudinal fins made from steel of the same section as the aluminium used in the façade structure itself. The result is a striking unity between the different elements of the façade and gives the clear impression of subtle forethought.

Further reading

Concrete Quarterly, No. 172, Spring 1992, pp. 19–21
Architectural Review, May 1992, pp. 44–53
Arup Journal, Vol. 26 No. 3, Autumn 1991, pp. 3–10

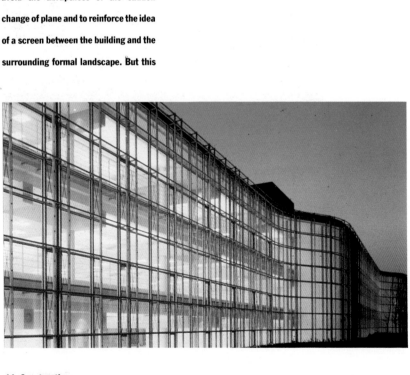

ITN Building

London 1990

Structural engineer: John Hirst
Ove Arup & Partners

Architect: Foster Associates
Client: Stanhope Properties

During the office boom of the 1980s the belief grew that in-situ reinforced concrete was too slow to satisfy the tight deadlines demanded by developers. However, the production process can nearly always be streamlined – if only more clients were enlightened enough to give architects and structural engineers the opportunity to spend the time necessary to achieve what is required. At the new headquarters building for ITN, work was able to begin on site just one week after the contract was signed, and the ten-storey structural frame was completed within about 26 weeks.

This remarkable speed was achieved by careful attention to the minute details of production and activity sequences early in the design stage in order to simplify and rationalise construction. Particular attention was given to activities lying on the critical path in the construction programme.

First came a decision about the foundations and basement. After a preliminary site investigation it became clear that, if the new building could be made light enough, it would be possible to build it on a raft placed over the foundations of the previous building; otherwise, deep, costly and time-consuming

piles would have to be driven. Although concrete frames are often considered too heavy to use where lightness is needed, this was not found to be the case here, and the architects' preference for concrete – particularly for its aesthetic qualities and ability to accommodate major reservicing during the building's life – could be met.

The site investigation, however, was not able to establish with sufficient confidence whether the retaining walls to the existing basement would be sufficiently strong and watertight. Rather than wait while further, more costly, site investigation was carried out (and which

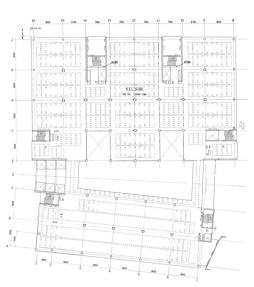

would not necessarily prove the walls' adequacy), it was decided to use these existing walls only as a first barrier and to construct a new basement structure within them.

Above ground the critical construction activity was the vertical structure. The construction cycle time for each storey was limited by the structural cores around stairs, lifts and service ducts. Normally, time is lost while formwork, reinforcement and concrete are placed, and the formwork struck before a subsequent floor can be constructed. This obstacle was avoided in two ways. The cores themselves were designed to be constructed as easily and quickly as possible: all ribs and returns were eliminated and closed boxes avoided, and the cores were finally conceived as a series of vertical flat slabs forming structurally efficient L- and H-sections to give the building its lateral stability. One proposal was to construct the main H-cores right up to roof level before embarking on the secondary cores and floors, but this idea became the victim of an earlier success: as a result of trim-

ming down the core sections the unrestrained walls of the cores would be so slender that they would need temporary support until stabilised by the rising floor structure. As a compromise, the cores were constructed just two or three storeys ahead of the floors, obviating the need for temporary support while also avoiding the delays inherent in a sequential wall-floor-wall approach.

The building frame itself was set out on two main grids. In addition to a number of architectural and planning advantages, this gave several structural and constructional benefits. The floor structure in each grid is a ribbed concrete slab with a virtually identical soffit in each bay so that large GRP moulds mounted on table-forms could be used to achieve rapid casting. The GRP forms consisted of a single main part with additional sections which could be added to accommodate occasional slight variations in edge details and slab thickness. The surface of the forms had a high-quality finish: much of the exposed structure is fair-faced concrete and the rest needed only minimal finishing and painting.

Dividing the building into two halves, either side of the central atrium, brought a further benefit. Since access to the site was restricted on all sides, the atrium provided a clear space in which to handle the construction materials and, especially, to manoeuvre the large table-forms by crane from one bay or floor to the next.

Although these were the main ways in which construction time was reduced, there were also many minor ones, including:

- detailing all structural sections to allow easy prefabrication of the steel reinforcement cages;
- keeping all staircases identical and precasting them off site;
- designing several major items to be independent of other parts of the structure so that their construction would not be on the critical path.

An example of the latter were the post-tensioned link bridges joining the two halves of the building across the atrium. These were designed to be installed after the structural frame was complete so that no time would be lost waiting for the concrete to develop sufficient strength to carry the post-tensioning forces. Because of their exposed position, particular care had to be taken to ensure the post-tensioning did not induce any positive or negative camber.

The glazing of the south face of the atrium, the so-called cathedral wall, was also designed for rapid construction. Wind loads are carried by the horizontal, prefabricated, steel box-beams (similar to those supporting the atrium roof) which span the 14 metres between the two halves of the building. A grid of RHS steel tubes stabilises these beams and supports the glazing. Both structure and glazing were installed upwards from ground level to avoid the need for temporary support.

The result is an exposed-concrete frame which is striking in its simplicity and elegance. The sculptural quality of solid concrete is exploited to the full – in columns, edge beams, soffits to the floor slabs, and the cantilevers projecting into the atrium from the main floors. The quality of the finish resembles that achieved by a stone mason – or precast concrete – rather than that usually associated with in-situ concrete. Yet, despite the crafted finish, the aesthetic of manufacturing and production is everywhere in evidence, both in the details and overall.

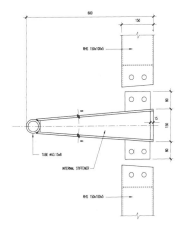

Further reading

<u>Arup Journal</u>, Vol. 26 No. 1, Spring 1991, pp. 20–23
<u>Concrete Quarterly</u>, Vol. 168, Spring 1991, pp. 16–19

Inland Revenue Offices

Nottingham 1993

Structural engineer John Thornton, **Ove Arup & Partners**

Architect: Michael Hopkins & Partners
Client: Inland Revenue

Elegance and simplicity seldom come about by chance; they must generally be set early on as a specific goal, and much experience, effort and skill must be directed towards achieving that goal. With hindsight it is easy to suppose that a simple solution to a design problem was obvious – 'I could have thought of that.'

To do this is often to render invisible the very process of design and, unfortunately, is a habit common among non-designers.

What could be simpler, then, than the superstructure of the Inland Revenue offices?

1 Prepare the site and foundations ready for columns.

2 Construct the building cores of in-situ concrete.

3 Deliver and erect fully-finished brickwork columns, working away from the cores.

4 Deliver and erect fully-finished precast-concrete floor slabs.

5 Repeat steps 3 and 4 for second and third floors.

Perhaps not quite that simple, but certainly an important step forward in showing how building construction can benefit from the lessons of production

engineering learnt in other industries. With intelligence and forethought it is not inevitable that off-site manufacture and prefabrication produce identical components and monotonous buildings.

The production process for the brickwork columns was conceived to enable a range of similar but different units to be created.

The steel and timber formwork for the precast-concrete vaults was made in sections. A series of inserts allowed for variations such as the end details or holes for light fittings. In this manner nearly 900 units, in two basic sizes with a total of 120 variants, could be manu-

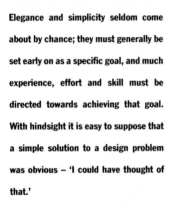

factured economically and with a high-quality surface finish.

The vaulted ceiling has its ancestry in the brick jack-arches spanning between the cast- or wrought-iron beams that were so ubiquitous in 19th-century warehouses and mills. But the similarity between the two systems is little more than geometric. In the mills the vault is an arch both in form and structural action, and the iron beams seldom span more than 3 or 4 metres between iron columns and masonry walls; the walls provide the lateral stability. The modern concrete 'vault' is actually a folded-plate slab that spans some 13 metres between

masonry columns; lateral stability is provided by the in-situ-concrete cores.

The shape of the concrete vaults had another derivation. Modern fire regulations limit the minimum thickness of a concrete slab to 95 mm; taking into account the ease of getting the steel and concrete into the formwork, the minimum practical thickness is about 130 mm. But a slab that thin could span no more than about 3 metres. How, then, could this minimum thickness of concrete be used to form a lightweight beam that was stiff and strong enough to span the full 13 metres? The solution was to increase the stiffness of the section (second moment of area) by corrugating the slab. What could be simpler?

Further reading

The Architects' Journal, 16 June 1993, pp. 41–52

Montreuil Sports Stadium

near Paris 1993

Structural engineer   <u>Marc Mimram</u>

Architect   <u>Marc Mimram</u>
Project associate   <u>Christophe Barthelemy (Architect)</u>
Client   <u>Montreuil Town Council</u>

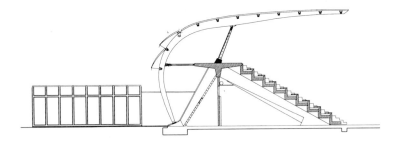

This municipal sports complex comprises three elements: changing facilities, the stand (beneath which are all the common facilities), and a roof to shelter the spectators. All are clearly differentiated, both in location and in the manner of their construction. The changing rooms at the rear are formed by six small and independent metal-clad concrete-wall 'boxes', the stands are built from in-situ reinforced-concrete portals supporting precast-concrete seating, and the roof is supported on ten pairs of curved steel box-girders with varying cross-sections.

Such is the complexity of the form of these sections that it is no exaggeration to say that the building could not have been designed or fabricated at an economic cost without the direct data link between the computer drawings and the computer-controlled cutting and welding equipment. By this means it was possible to create the form of the building elements almost in the manner of a sculptor working directly with the steel.

Although the metal frame which supports the roof contrasts with the con-

crete portals of the stands, they were nevertheless conceived to form a coherent structure. The two elements are articulated both at their common base and at the foot of the V-shaped struts which support the upper ends of the main roof ribs and provide longitudinal stability.

The roofing itself comprises three skins with distinct functions:

- the centre layer is a galvanised self-stiffened metal sheet and forms the waterproof layer;
- the upper layer of tensioned white aluminium sheets gives the roof a continuous external finish;
- the under side is faced with treated plywood panels which give a unity to the volume of the stand.

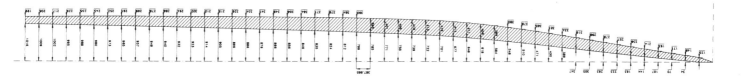

The main curved ribs are manufactured entirely from flat steel plates and fabricated using computer-controlled cutting and welding machinery. This technique is now widely available and can enable a designer to create complex geometric forms such as a continuously variable cross-section and, hence, section stiffness (second moment of area). A steel structure can thus be given a form which faithfully reflects the loads it must carry.

Each curved box-girder rib comprises 13 sections, each of which is bounded by four uniquely curved faces. Since the lines of intersection between these 52 surfaces cannot be defined as parts of simple geometrical curves, it would not have been possible to mark them out with sufficient accuracy on the steel plate prior to cutting. The CAD computer was programmed to calculate the co-ordinates of a large number of points along the edges and feed these directly to the computers controlling the oxy-acetylene cutting tools. The steel plates are joined by a continuous weld in the exposed angle formed where one plate overhangs the other at right-angles.

A similar technique was used to manufacture the V-shaped struts which stabilise the cantilever roof ribs and the horizontal ties between the ribs and concrete stand, both of which help to give shape to the volume that forms the upper promenade of the stand. They, too, feature a varying section, though it was created in a different way. Two steel tubes of different radii were cut longitudinally at an angle and welded together to form a closed section. The connections between the struts and the roof rib they support are also made of sheet steel, cut and welded to create a three-dimensional form which exploits the inherent in-plane stiffness while sufficiently reducing the unsupported areas of plate to avoid local buckling.

Fabricating the ribs and struts from sheet steel at once allows an expression of the structural form – the functions of the individual components and the manufacturing properties of the material – as well as providing an opportunity to display the sculptural quality of exposed joints and members. The art of cutting and welding the steel plate itself becomes part of the architectural vocabulary.

Schlumberger
Cambridge Research

Phase 2 1992

Structural engineer **Buro Happold**

Architect **Michael Hopkins & Partners**

Client **Schlumberger Cambridge Research**

Anyone who has watched the timber formwork for floor beams and slabs being cut to size, erected, and dismantled, must have wondered if there wasn't an easier and less labour-intensive way to mould concrete in the late-20th century: the process can have changed little since the Romans built the Pantheon. Sometimes it may be that there is no better way. More often the answer is that the production engineering issues for concrete have been poorly addressed at the design stage.

Devising a way of producing concrete efficiently is a matter of balancing a number of incompatible variables: the benefits of a high-quality finish straight from the mould, the ease of getting concrete into its final location in liquid form, the convenience of working in factory conditions rather than on site, the wish to achieve variation of form rather than monotony.

Several projects in this book illustrate a number of ways in which these conflicting issues can be reconciled with ingenuity and imagination to produce attractive, high-quality, high-speed and cost-effective buildings in concrete. Yet another technique is the use of permanent formwork; and since the formwork can be made of concrete, the appearance of the finished building can be true to its construction.

The designers of the Schlumberger building were partly inspired by Pier Luigi Nervi, the engineer who, in the late 1940s, first exploited the idea of permanent formwork and developed a suitable material from which to make the

forms – ferrocemento. Like concrete, this is a composite, made from a thin mortar with steel-mesh reinforcement resembling chicken wire. Since Nervi's time, glass-reinforced cement has been used in a similar manner but in this project it proved more costly than ferrocemento without significant advantages.

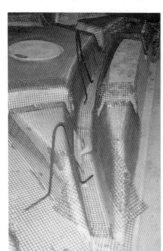

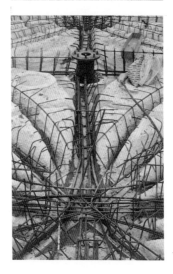

The use of ferrocemento in buildings brings many benefits. Nowadays the forms are made in factory conditions in moulds of glass-reinforced plastic or even ferrocemento itself, and extremely high-quality finishes can be achieved, partly since no aggregate is used. In this building the largest ferrocemento forms

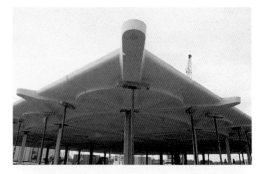

Ground floor ceiling ribs

 Ground floor columns   First floor columns

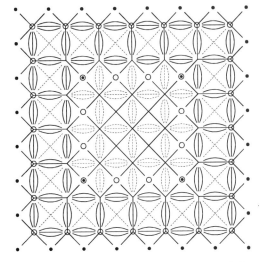

—— Primary structural ribs   --- Secondary structural ribs

Structure of first floor slab

were 3.6 metres square and, with a shell thickness of between 25 and 50 mm, great care was needed to prevent damage during their transport to site and erection in situ. The forms were propped until the floor was cast and able to bear its own weight. It was necessary to be especially vigilant when supervising the placing of the rib- and slab-reinforcement since the work-force was not familiar with this type of construction. Nevertheless, the production process on

site went smoothly and the quality of the result repaid the investment in design development.

Continuously varying profiles can be achieved more easily with precast permanent formwork than with conventional in-situ concrete. To exploit this advantage to the full, a complex though regular pattern had to be conceived to resolve several competing influences. There was obvious benefit in having as few different moulds as possible and eventually the entire floor slab was made from only five different forms. The rib pattern also needed to take account of three different grids in the floor plan: the column grid at ground level, the column grid at first-floor level (much of which is displaced by half a bay relative to the ground floor), and the grids for lighting and air conditioning in the ground-floor ceiling.

A pattern was finally developed combining two overlapping grids at 45° to one another. These grids are expressed in the ribs of the floor slab, which are also shaped to hint at the directions of the lines of principal stress (isostatics)

and the load paths through the slabs to the columns beneath. Although they are used with great architectural effect, as with Nervi's precedent, they are not to be taken too literally. While isostatic maps would be true to stresses in a homogenous flat slab, load paths in a ribbed slab will flow along the stiffest route – the ribs themselves. A classic case of 'archi-structure', but none the worse for it.

The aesthetic of the casting process is again celebrated, in iron, at roof level. Above the irregular grid of the first-floor columns, the architects wanted a regular pattern on the exposed steelwork of the roof structure. This idea evolved into a grillage of steel beams, identical in length and section, supported at some intersections but not others. A means had to be developed for joining four beams at internal nodes, with or without a column beneath, and at the asymmetric junction of three beams and a façade column. A casting was the preferred solution to ensure that stresses would flow smoothly through the component from one member to another without causing stress concentrations.

Malleable cast iron – also called ductile or spheroidal graphite cast iron after the shape of the carbon inclusions which break up the otherwise regular crystalline structure of the iron and act as crack stoppers – was chosen. Like traditional cast iron, the recently developed spheroidal graphite (SG) cast iron is easy to cast in intricate shapes but, unlike its ancestor, is strong in both

The glazing bars which span a full 3 metres between floor and ceiling are given a lightness of touch by making them as miniature Vierendeel girders.

compression and tension and is not brittle. It can therefore be used in highly stressed applications without the fear of sudden brittle fracture and the catastrophic collapses which led to the demise of structural cast iron in the late 1840s. In this application SG cast iron was preferred to cast steel because it was cheaper, it has better flow characteristics when molten (intricate shapes can be achieved more easily and a better finish can be obtained), and no welding was needed (SG cast iron cannot be welded satisfactorily). As in so many of our Victorian mills, the result is an elegant, sculptured component, albeit, in this instance, rather difficult to see in the finished building.

Further reading

The Architects' Journal, 28 October 1992, pp. 31–42
Proceedings of 4th International Conference on Space Structures, University of Surrey, Thomas Telford 1993, pp. 1443–1450

Justification

The term 'justification' includes all the means which an engineer may use to confirm his belief that the structural idea he has conceived will work, and that it will be safe, use no more material than necessary, and not succumb to any foreseeable failures.

Early in a project an engineer will derive sufficient confidence in a proposed structure from his feel for materials and structural behaviour. This knowledge, gained from hands-on experience, precedent, and observation, will enable the engineer to make confident qualitative predictions about the likely behaviour of a new structure. When more accurate confirmation is required there are two principal means of obtaining this. Most common structures can be tested using mathematical models based on well-proven theories of engineering science. The interpretation of such models also involves a lot of empirical data that has been gathered over the years, and together they form the core of the many design procedures that have been developed, such as the new Eurocodes.

For many structures or structural elements, however, the use of mathematical models is inadequate, unreliable, inappropriate, or too complex and costly; the modern engineer shares this much with his medieval ancestor. In these circumstances – and it takes considerable experience and good engineering judgement to recognise them – the engineer must seek additional confirmation by other methods, in particular the testing of models or even full-scale tests.

Physical tests may be done for many different reasons. Often they are needed to establish loads on structures: wind-tunnel tests, loads caused by earthquakes. On other occasions it is the effect of loads that is at issue: natural frequencies and the character of vibrations, fatigue and creep behaviour of materials, deflections and surface strains of components (strain cannot be measured inside a material and stress cannot be measured directly at all). Models can also be used to establish the most appropriate shape of some structures – cable-net and membrane structures, compression arches, vaults and shells. Finally, physical models are often used to establish and confirm manufacturing and assembly procedures.

It is essential that this process of justification leaves nothing out. Every aspect of structural behaviour must be checked – dimensions, area of cross-section, second moment of area, levels of stress and strain in materials, deflections and movements, stability, collapse mechanisms, ultimate load-carrying capacity, and so on. All this must be done for every component and sub-assembly as well as for the entire structure and its interaction with both the services and building envelope. Every potentially damaging load and load combination must be considered.

By these means the engineer needs to gain sufficient confidence in every aspect of a structure to sign a piece of paper indicating his conviction. The outcome is, ultimately, a document containing calculations, test results and the engineer's interpretation of all the data. This will be submitted for independent checking to confirm the engineer's level of confidence. But the document alone is not enough; in large measure the confidence is implicit in the professionalism of the design engineers and checking engineers.

Ultimately, if a structure is to be realised at all, a convincing means of justifying predictions of its behaviour is essential. If no such means is known, the structural engineer must devise one; if one cannot be devised, it would be foolhardy to build the structure.

Having conceived a structure in terms of a given material, one then has recourse to one technique or another to see if it is going to stand up or not. … One of the ways of doing this is to analyse the stresses mathematically. There are many other ways. One is to build a structure and see if it falls down. Another is to make a model and test it … you still have to know, as you do when you are undertaking mathematical analysis, what questions you want to ask, which means you must understand your structure first.

Alan Harris

Usine L'Oréal, Paris

1992

Structural engineer	Richard Hough, Mike Banfi
	Ove Arup & Partners International
Architect	Valode et Pistre et Associés
Client	L'Oréal

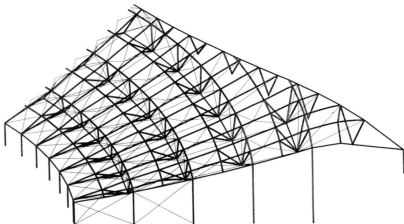

The image chosen for the roof of L'Oréal's new factory was of the petals of a white flower draped over the three clear-span space-frame structures that house the manufacturing areas.

In order to provide an open floor space it was decided to support the roof structure only at its perimeter and, as a consequence, the largest radial spans are around 60 metres. A two-way spanning structure was chosen to minimise its weight. The resulting space-frame comprises a grid of radial V-shaped trusses and circumferential planar trusses and has a simple, homogenous expression which reflects that of the roof panels above. Within the space-frame pattern, inverted square-based pyramids were chosen as key visual elements, seeming to prop the petals with

their sets of four tubular fingers.

The presence of the pyramids in the space-frame geometry is accentuated by maximising the use of tension members in the surrounding structure, leaving the tube pyramids apparently suspended in space. This makes for a rather more subtle structural behaviour than might at first be supposed. Different combinations of the tension members are used to carry the forces arising from the different load conditions which may act on the roof. Since the slender tie-rods can-

not carry loads in compression, the computer model of the structure used for studying member forces and deflections had to be non-linear. Thus, as changing loads might reduce the force in a tie to zero, any further change would result in the member effectively disappearing from the model since it cannot carry compression.

Between the scheme design stage and final agreements with the steelwork contractor, wind-tunnel testing was undertaken in order to justify the

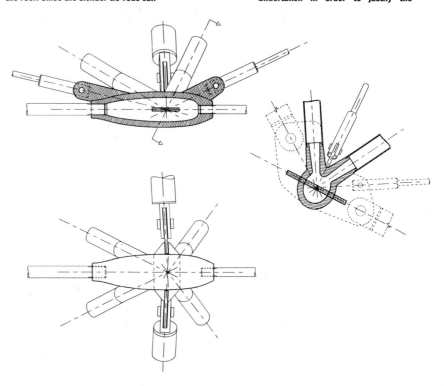

assumptions that had been made about uplift loads on the roof due to the wind. This resulted in a net saving to the client as the reduction in the amount of steel used in the roof more than covered the cost of the tests and additional structural analysis.

Many tubes and rods meet at the apexes of the pyramids. Most of these nodes join the four fingers, two circumferential tubes and six tie-rods at various angles – 12 members in all – and, to prevent rotation, the centre lines of the members must all meet at a single point. This joint is an important visual focus in sculptural terms and its shape was developed to reinforce the structural theme of 'tubes-dominant, ties-recessive'. A steel casting was chosen to bring sufficient mass of steel to the joint to

carry the forces while allowing its form to be sensitively sculpted. The radial tie-rods screw into the casting while other tie-rods are linked by pins to gusset plates welded to its surface. The circumferential tubular members are connected to a plate which passes through the hollow centre of the joint. This allows the wall thickness of the casting, the main body of which is 265 mm in diameter and 850 mm long, to be substantially reduced down to just 32 mm.

For such an unusual component it was judged that theoretical studies alone would not give sufficient justification of its structural behaviour or the magnitude of any stress concentrations within the casting. A trial joint was loaded on a specially-built test rig and gauges were used to measure the strain

in the surface of the casting, especially in likely areas of stress concentration. From these measurements a reliable picture of the flow of stresses within the steel itself was built up; in particular, stress levels at the points of stress concentration were confirmed as meeting the criteria for avoiding local failure due to metal fatigue. The castings were also proved capable of withstanding twice their anticipated service load without suffering permanent deformation.

Further reading

Le moniteur, No. 4652, 22 January 1993
Arup Journal, Vol. 27 No. 3, Autumn 1992, pp. 11–13

Albert Dock
Liverpool 1842–48/1982–88

Structural engineer Jesse Hartley

Curtins Consulting Engineers

Client Merseyside Development Corporation

The 19th century has left Britain with a wonderful legacy of commercial and industrial buildings – warehouses, mills and factories, made of brick or stone combined with cast iron and wrought iron. These materials are very durable and it is a sign of relatively enlightened times that the cry 'if it's old, knock it down', so prevalent in the 1960s and '70s, is heard less often today. There is now no excuse for demolishing buildings that are structurally adequate and which, with a modicum of architectural and engineering skill and sensitivity, can be transformed to suit a range of viable modern uses.

The issue of structural adequacy is, however, a deep subject and one which is all too easily misunderstood. Using a narrow definition – would the building entirely satisfy a modern code of practice? – most 19th-century buildings would probably be condemned; after all, modern codes cater only for modern materials and construction details. At the other extreme, it is clearly unwise to argue simply that if a building is still standing it must be safe. Between these two extremes there are many subtle variations.

The iron structure which supports the masonry vaults of Jesse Hartley's ware-

house buildings on the Liverpool waterfront is unique. The ingenious cross-sections and sculptured forms make it one of the most remarkable examples of the use of cast iron in building. Given this and their imposing site, these dock buildings were clearly worth preserving and are, indeed, Grade I listed.

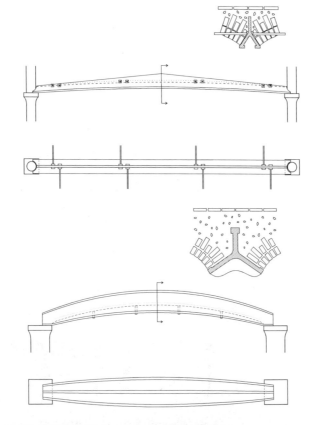

However, although the floors were originally designed to withstand about 15 kN/m^2, an initial assessment of the structure suggested that the adequacy of some of the floors could not be justified using a rigorous application of modern codes. The main reason was that the conservative value for the tensile strength of cast iron, which is generaly recommended, is extremely low. Similar initial conclusions were drawn concerning some of the masonry walls, the integrity of the iron structure, and the piled foundations, none of which would quite satisfy the modern codes. And yet the buildings gave every appearance of being very robust and, despite heavy use, had survived with little distress for nearly 140 years.

An alternative approach was taken and some of the assumptions behind the initial assessment were examined more carefully. For instance, although there was evidence of corrosion, more detailed investigations established that it did not penetrate very deeply beneath the surface; the structural cross-section was thus not as seriously weakened as had been feared. Also, samples of cast iron taken from beams throughout the building were found to be of a higher quality and strength than it is usually recommended to assume. It was also concluded that the iron beams were sufficiently well bonded to the masonry vaults to enable these two structural elements to act compositely rather than separately, allowing the floors to carry heavier loads.

Similarly, thorough investigations were made on the masonry vaults and piled foundations and sample testing was undertaken to establish more realistic assumptions on which to base an assessment of the strength and stability of the actual structure. Finally, the validity of the whole approach was checked by undertaking full-scale load tests on key parts of the entire structure.

With all this particular evidence about the actual structure and its behaviour, the engineers were able to make a convincing argument, using both modern and old Codes of Practice, that the building could be made structurally adequate with relatively little intervention

and that most of the original structure could thus be retained and restored.

The roof, which spans up to 50 feet, is of an unusual construction and proved rather trickier to justify than other parts of the building. The tiles are of $^3/_{16}''$ wrought-iron sheet rather than the more usual stone or clay; the wrought-iron truss is not of a common design (indeed it is not really a truss as we now use the word) and the usual purlins are absent. The first analysis of this structure, based

on the assumption that it worked as an ordinary tiled roof, led to the surprising conclusion that the roof should not still be standing! It is at this point that an insensitive engineer would have condemned the structure. A more intelligent one doubted the assumptions, not his eyes.

It finally became clear that the roof must be working in a manner that was not obvious from first impressions. The wrought-iron cladding was found to be acting as a stressed skin and working compositely with the trusses, rather in the manner of a modern folded-plate structure. In fact, like the iron beams, this particular roof construction is unique and it is tantalising to wonder if Hartley or a colleague conceived of the roof working in this way. For today's engineers, by accepting that there must be at least one way in which the roof might be working, it was possible to declare that it would remain structurally adequate – on condition, of course, that appropriate care was taken to ensure that it could continue to work as a structure in this same way.

Further reading

The Structural Engineer, Vol. 64A No. 10, October 1986, pp. 283–290 Nancy Ritchie-Noakes, Liverpool's Historic Waterfront, 1984 Architectural Review, July 1988, pp. 18–27 (similar building – Tate of the North) 'Structural appraisal of existing buildings for change of use', BRE Digest 366, 1991

London Underwriting Centre

Structural engineer Robin Adams
YRM-Anthony Hunt Associates

Architects YRM-Anthony Hunt Associates
Client The London Underwriting Centre

3 Minster Court, London 1993

Building designers are constantly faced with two incompatible goals – the wish to innovate and the need to be certain that the innovation will perform as intended and conceived. This is the root cause of much of the risk associated with all construction projects. Risk is always highest when someone plans to do something thought not to be new, but which turns out to depart from precedent in unforeseen ways (a common example of this is using materials in new and untried combinations). However, when designers <u>know</u> they are innovating it is always possible to take intelligent steps to reduce the risk to acceptable levels.

Suspending sixteen escalators from a ring beam at roof level had not been attempted before. The idea arose from

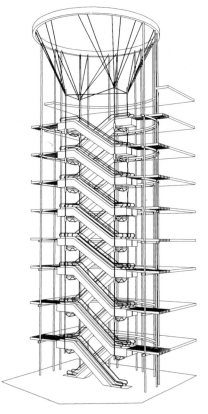

the frustration of having to wait for lifts in a business environment where speed of movement in the building is essential. An added bonus with escalators in an open atrium is that it is possible to see where people are.

In itself, the 152-tonne weight of the suspended structure, in addition to the weight of passengers, posed little problem – the four high-tensile steel rods are just 48 mm in diameter at the bottom of the stack, increasing to 90 mm at the top. More challenging was the need to justify the safety and viability of the structure in two particular sets of adverse conditions: the horrific possibility of one of the rods failing, and vibrations being set up either in part of or the whole structure – every schoolboy knows how to set a light, pedestrian bridge in

violent motion. It is through the engineer's ability to imagine all manner of possible structural accidents, and devising means of demonstrating how the structure can deal with them safely, that the potential risks of innovation can be reduced.

Each escalator rests at either end on a light steel truss, which in turn spans between two of the tie-rods. The four tie-rods are each suspended, via a large cast-steel node and six inclined hangers, from a box-girder ring-beam made from steel plate. The ring-beam rests on sixteen tubular steel columns which carry loads down to a transfer structure at atrium-floor level and thence to the foundations. 'Butterfly bracing' connects the four nodes to fix in space the main points of support for the escalator stack. At each of the nine levels, two landing grillages connect the escalators to the main floor structure to restrain the suspended system in the horizontal direction and prevent it swinging or twisting about a vertical axis.

Although a good horizontal connection is required between the landing grillages and the escalator stack, care had to be taken to reduce the vertical loads being carried by the grillages rather than the four main ties. This was achieved by two means. A sliding joint was used to take up any relative movements during construction, before being bolted through vibration-mountings in its final position. Also, the system was prestressed by raising the entire suspended structure by an amount equal to the deflection it would experience when fully loaded with passengers. Thus, with no passengers on the escalators, the grillages are slightly stressed in an upwards direction; when the escalators are fully loaded, the load on the grillages is reduced to zero.

The reason for this prestressing lies in the second important function performed by the landing grillages: they are designed to be strong enough to support the whole escalator stack should one of the four tie-rods fail, although, in this condition, the grillages would experience large deflections which would be acceptable only in an emergency. It was thus vital that the grillages should carry no downward load in normal use in order that their function as a viable fail-safe support could be satisfactorily justified.

The design procedure that provided

this justification involved consideration of the many different load paths which might be needed to carry the large variety of possible loads on the structure and its components safely down to the foundations – during construction, in normal use and in the event of any of the structural components failing. A fire-engineering study of the atrium space demonstrated that the escalator structure was likely to be subjected to only a small fire load and the $1^{1}/_{2}$-hour fire rating was achieved using intumescent paint on only the twenty-four inclined hangers at roof level.

Since the structure is lightweight, exposed and relatively undamped, and must support several large moving machines and perhaps a hundred people running, it was recognised that the effect of dynamic loads would need to be investigated thoroughly. The most severe challenge for the design engineers was to ensure and justify an acceptable performance of the structure in the face of these various dynamic loads. The principal objectives were to avoid long-term resonance in the support structure, which could lead to a fatigue failure in the material from which the main load-bearing connections are made, and to ensure that any short-term resonance would be of a frequency and magnitude that users of the escalators would not find uncomfortable. This was achieved by first considering the frequencies of the likely dynamic loads – normal pedestrian movements, the escalator machinery, and accidental loads such as people jumping on the

escalators. These sources of possible excitation were then compared with calculated estimates of the natural frequencies of the escalator trusses and the main supporting structure. A design specification for the atrium support structure was thus derived. It was calculated that the natural frequency of the critical structural elements should be greater than 4.5 Hz (cycles per second) and not lie within the 10–15 Hz band.

However, it was considered that educated estimates of the loads and calculated estimates of the natural frequencies of the structural elements during the design stage did not provide an adequate justification of the performance of the finished structure. To raise confidence in the design calculations, the structure was tested at two stages during production: the vibration characteristics of an escalator were measured in the fabrication shop, and the natural frequencies and dynamic response of the entire structure and its components were measured in situ before coming into public use. The results were found to be close enough to the estimates to confirm the justification calculations.

Further reading

New Builder, 8 October 1993, pp. 16–17
Architectural Review, November 1993, pp. 181–191

New Square

Bedfont Lakes, Surrey 1992

Structural engineer   <u>Buro Happold</u>

Architect   <u>Michael Hopkins & Partners</u>

Client   <u>MEPC/IBM UK</u> joint venture

Steel has an enormous number of qualities: it is the strongest conventional construction material and has many production engineering advantages (it can be rolled into sections, cast, and joined by welding or bolting) and, with good corrosion protection, it can maintain its elegant looks for a long life. Steel's major disadvantage is that its strength is severely reduced by heat from fires.

In most applications this disadvantage is overcome by using steel sections rather larger than otherwise needed, or by protecting the surface of the metal from direct contact with fire by sprayed coatings, boards or concrete. During the last decade or so the use of intumescent paints has allowed 'exposed' steelwork to be used in more and more circumstances. Nevertheless, engineers are constantly challenged to reduce steel sections to an absolute minimum for both visual and economic reasons, and original thinking is needed to 'stretch' the material still further.

For the IBM headquarters at Bedfont Lakes the architects wanted to create a building with an exposed-steel finish.

They were also keen to retain the metal's crisp surface texture which is usually diminished under layers of intumescent paint. To achieve this goal the engineers could not adopt the conventional approach to fire protection. Normally, satisfactory fire performance for a steel structure is achieved by covering the

metal with an insulating layer that is thick enough to reduce temperatures on the inner face of the insulation to acceptable levels. But such an approach is very conservative: it takes no account of precisely how the steel heats up in a fire, or the reduced, but still useful, strength of steel at fire temperatures.

During the last decade or so a more rational 'fire-engineering' approach to the fire performance of steel has been developed. This involves a fundamentally different philosophy for designing critical elements in steel, in particular in the way the adequacy of the structure is justified by a rational argument supported, where appropriate, by calculations. A number of 'limit states' for the steel can be defined, beyond which performance in a fire will be inadequate;

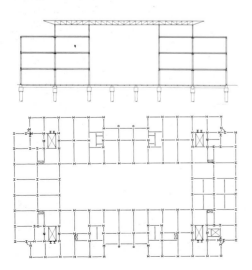

anywhere within these boundaries will be satisfactory.

In many ways this new approach to fire and its effect on a structure is analogous to a consideration of loads acting on buildings. A force-load acting at a certain point in a structure gives rise to stresses within the material which are carried along load paths to foundations; en route, stress levels, bending moments and deflections must be kept below predefined limits. In a fire, fire-loads act on exposed surfaces of material, raising its temperature, and the heat is conducted along heat paths to cooler parts of the building. The performance of the structure in a fire depends entirely on the strength of the steel, and this in turn is determined by its temperature. The fire-engineering approach focuses directly on the temperature of the steel and how this varies at different depths within the structural section, at different places in the structure, and at different times during the fire. Knowing the temperatures of the metal, a useful estimate can thus be made of the strength and stability of key elements and of the entire structure.

Direct consequences of this approach include the obvious benefits of reducing the size of the potential fire load (both in magnitude and duration), using thicker steel sections which can conduct heat away from hot-spots more effectively, minimising the area of steel exposed to the fire, and encouraging airflow to prevent the creation of local hot-spots.

At Bedfont Lakes the exposed columns and edge beams of the external and atrium façades were the most critical areas. The inside face of the columns were fire-protected by board while the inside of the edge beams and most of the floor steel were embedded in concrete.

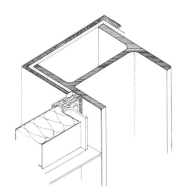

Following the fire-engineering approach, it was decided to create the façade edge beams from Universal Column sections rather than Universal Beams. These have three advantages

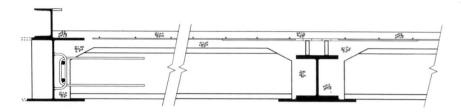

over beams of equivalent I-value (second moment of area): the minimum thickness of metal and the area of the section are greater, and the ratio of the area of steel exposed to heat, to the total area of the section (H_p/A in fire-engineering jargon) is smaller. Thus, in a given fire, the temperature at the heart of the section will be lower and hence structurally more useful, and the temperature of the metal will rise more slowly.

In fact, the façade edge beams are created from two sections: a Universal Column section, 305 x 305, with a channel section welded to the upper flange. The outer edges of the flanges of the column section are trimmed back to avoid an excessive depth back to the web. The element thus assumes proportions more typical of a Universal Beam section and helps to create the appearance of structural delicacy that is characteristic of the building's façade. The concrete planks are firmly connected to the inner face of the edge-beam web and the void filled with concrete to ensure that the beam would work compositely with the

floor and not suffer from twisting due to the eccentric load on the flange.

A great deal of computer analysis was needed to model the fire performance of this complex cross-section, but the result was that it was possible to justify its safety with no need to apply fire protection at all. An extremely elegant façade structure has been created which will perform satisfactorily in a fire – thick sections with low H_p/A are used; the parts of the steel structure subject to the highest stresses are embedded in concrete; exposed steel is kept to a minimum and to areas where it achieves its architectural effect; and only a small proportion of the structural steel needs to be fire-protected in conventional ways.

Although fire was also an issue in the floor structure of the building, its construction was influenced mainly by the building services. The building was to be occupied by a computer-intensive occupant (IBM) who wanted a highly controllable and flexible air-conditioning system. This was achieved by using a large number of units, each linked by its

own small duct to the space it serves. A direct consequence of this, together with the provision for additional installations in the future, was that there would be an unusually high density of ducts leaving the core areas. Any floor structure which employed either downstand ribs in the soffit or protruding steel beams, even if castellated, would have led to difficulties with servicing.

The use of 9-metre pre-cast-, pre-stressed-concrete planks was attractive in view of the long spans possible and the speed with which they can be erected and carry loads. In order to minimise the depth of the supporting structure and to avoid downstands, the planks could rest on the upper side of the lower flanges of steel beams. However, to span the required 6 metres, a steel beam would have needed to be much deeper than the concrete planks.

An effective solution for the primary floor beams was found to be a composite section comprising a 203 x 203 Universal Column section, to the underside of which was welded an additional 15 mm-steel plate, 410 mm wide. Since

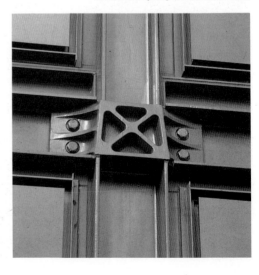

the concrete planks rest on the protruding plate, the difficulty of inserting planks between the beam flanges was avoided. Shear studs are welded to the top flange of the beam and tied to the reinforcement in the concrete topping in order to achieve fully composite action of the whole floor structure. By this means it was possible to span 6 metres with a steel section just 203 mm deep.

Most of the cross-section of the floor beams was to be embedded in concrete and fire protection was not an issue. It was decided to protect the exposed surface of the steel plate using fire-board. While design and construction proceeded, British Steel undertook a number of fire tests which demonstrated that the exposed surface would not, in fact, need fire protection. This was later confirmed by a theoretical fire-engineering study involving the computer modelling of the temperature levels and heat flow in the composite section when subjected to a range of plausible fire loads. These results were too late to affect the construction of the IBM building, but the success of the approach has been established and similar composite sections are now being promoted as a highly efficient way of using steel.

As a steel building through and through, two further structural details are worthy of note. Throughout the building the architects wanted the columns to reflect the size of load they carry and the transition between different sections at different floors is pointed up by an ornate casting. Although thirty differently-shaped castings were originally planned for the entire building, it would have proved too costly to have them all made. Various design details were modified and rationalised so that finally just six different patterns were needed by the foundry. As malleable cast iron cannot be welded satisfactorily, cast steel was chosen. The different nodes and column sections were welded together in the fabrication shop and brought to site as full-height columns.

Steel also plays a part in providing the building with its lateral stability. This is provided not by the usual cross-bracing or concrete shear wall in the building cores, but by steel shear plates in the façade, based on the same module as the cladding. Although vertical fins are apparent, they are for appearance rather than stiffening: at 15 mm thick, in order to avoid visible distortion caused during the cutting and fabrication processes, the plates are more than thick enough to cope with wind loads by acting in tension across their diagonals.

One Off Studio

London 1991

Structural engineer **Atelier One**

Architect **Ron Arad Associates**

In designing new studio premises for their design and architecture practice, the architects wanted to achieve a sculptural quality for the entire building and to express this in the form, material and fabrication techniques. Nevertheless, as with all projects, statutory approvals and calculations must justify the structural design, particularly when an unusual material or structural idea forms part of the building's conception.

The shape of the columns was

strongly influenced by their various functions: they needed to achieve a rigid, moment-resisting connection with the curved roof beams, they were also to be fabricated from steel plate which would need to be braced to carry the compression loads and bending moments. Curved stiffening fins, welded

to the vertical plates, would also serve as the guide tracks for the 1-metre-high windows (rotating about a central horizontal axis) which were initially proposed. The end wall of the studio was also to be made of steel plate and this, too, would require stiffening ribs.

Close liaison with the engineers was necessary to enable the architects to create the desired sculptural, almost spontaneous quality of the different elements. In turn, the engineer had to ensure that the elements could provide the necessary resistance to local and overall buckling, and that suitable calculations could be provided to satisfy the local Building Control office. Thus, the architects were given certain dimensions – such as the minimum moment arm at the column-to-roof-beam con-

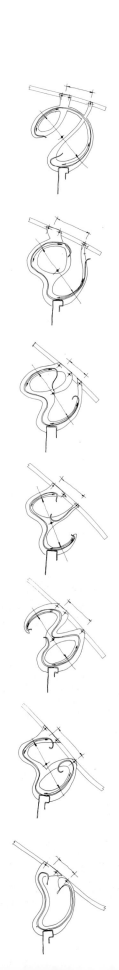

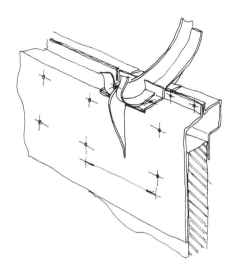

nection and the minimum spacing of stiffening ribs in the end wall which were necessary for structural reasons – and within these limitations they could exercise their own freedom.

The roof to the studio was also the result of close collaboration. The architects had wanted a three-dimensional form to span between the curved ribs and had found a metal mesh – Expamet – which could be shaped to give the desired soft quality to the roof surface. The problem was that on its

own it was not an adequate structural material. A membrane roof was also considered, but rejected to avoid the hi-tech cliché of fabric and cables.

The engineer conceived the idea of using mesh and fabric together – both could be suitably shaped and if the mesh could carry sufficient compression forces it could form a means of tensioning the membrane and avoiding unwanted cables. A series of tests established the mesh could be shaped to follow the form of the membrane precisely, with a separation of 80 mm, and would be able to carry adequate compression and shear forces to act as a thin (perforated) shell. These tests formed part of the justification to Building Control and also established that the mesh would be strong enough to act as a cantilever beyond the edge of the membrane and shade the flexible PVC glazing in the studio wall.

Since the most suitable form of compression shell under a certain set of loads is the same as that of a membrane subject to the opposite loads, the same design approach was adopted for both, using the same analysis software to find and justify the forms. There remained the careful calculation of the shapes of the individual sections of mesh and PVC-covered fabric which had to be joined to fit the unique shapes needed for each bay of the roof. Finally, a number of bespoke connection details were developed to join the mesh and fabric to the adjacent buildings and the curved steel ribs.

Further reading

One Off Three, Artemis, 1993

Structural engineer **Tony Fitzpatrick**

Ove Arup & Partners

Architect **Foster Associates**

Client **Century Tower Corporation**

When designing most buildings it is usual to ensure that the materials are not stressed beyond the limit of their elastic behaviour and that no foreseeable loads would cause permanent deformations. For high-rise buildings in an earthquake zone this requirement would be impossibly expensive to achieve. Three, more realistic, criteria are applied:

- for small earthquakes there should be no permanent damage to any part of the building;
- for moderate earthquakes there should be no permanent damage to the structure, but cladding and fittings may sustain damage;
- for the largest credible earthquake the structure must continue to stand, but may suffer permanent damage such as bending of major structural elements.

To survive a massive earthquake, the normal means of bracing a building frame, such as cross-bracing or K-bracing, cannot be used. If any triangulated structure is loaded to failure, the only possible failure mechanisms are all catastrophic – fracture in tension, buckling of elements in compression, or shearing of welds and bolts.

The only way a tall building can be designed to survive an earthquake is to allow part of the structure to deform in a non-catastrophic way and, most importantly, to do so by absorbing the kinetic energy which the earthquake imparts to the building. Fortunately, steel is an ideal material to perform this function. It is highly ductile and, as it is bent back and forth, absorbs a great deal of energy. This plastic behaviour of steel and its high-energy absorption (hysteresis) are similarly exploited in crash-resisting structures such as cars, motorway barriers and bomb shelters.

All these structural matters are enshrined in local building regulations and design codes which, in various ways, reflect the different local circumstances and attitudes of the engineering research and engineering design communities. The regulations and codes serve to ensure safety and indicate to designers how to achieve it. In particular, they stipulate how designers must confirm and demonstrate that they have designed a safe structure. In Tokyo, a number of practices are usual:

- high-rise buildings have heavy moment frames and safety is ensured by keeping stresses within prescribed limits;
- it is not acceptable that a building should show no damage at all after a medium earthquake which it is likely to sustain about every 40 years;
- there is a very stringent requirement for analytical proof and great emphasis is placed on the precise mathematical model of the load – especially the time-history of horizontal ground velocities (the model must be tested using data from three actual earthquakes);
- two models of the building must be studied in great depth: a complex model of one floor of the building and a simple 'stick model' of the entire building;
- since torsion effects are difficult or imprecise to predict using either model, design rules advocate the avoidance of torsion problems in building structures.

In California the maximum credible 'design earthquake' is very similar to that used in Japan, but there is a greater

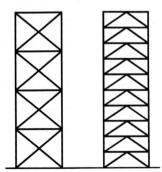

Braced frames <u>not</u> suitable for earthquake zones

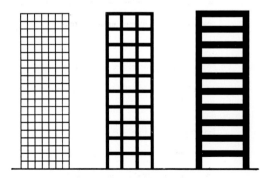

Vierendeel frames suitable for earthquake zones

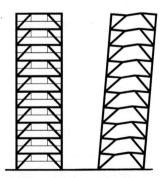

Behaviour of eccentrically-braced frame in earthquake

tolerance to non-structural damage caused by smaller earthquakes, which helps reduce the cost of the building. It is also acceptable to undertake a rather simpler analysis of a complex model of the entire building by using a less precise model of ground velocities and loads in actual earthquakes.

The most usual type of structure for earthquake resistant buildings is the Vierendeel frame. This derives its stability from rigid joints which can transfer bending moments from one member to another and, finally, to the foundations (or vice-versa in an earthquake!). Under large loads, the beams (but not columns) deform to create plastic hinges, but hinges that require considerable energy to rotate – thus, the existence of many hinges need not lead to collapse. However, to absorb enough energy, a large amount of steel needs to deform. This is generally arranged by having many small structural bays in the building. To achieve the same resistance with fewer bays, for instance to create open floor plans and large window areas, more and more massive beams and columns would be required, which would be both uneconomical and unsightly.

The small-bay Vierendeel frame is ubiquitous in all earthquake zones. Recently, however, an alternative approach to seismic design has been developed and used in California and, occasionally, in Japan. A modified version of the K-brace is used in the shear cores of a building. Part of the structure is triangulated and designed never to reach its yield stress. Between two such

triangulated sections is a series of ductile links which are intended to deform in an earthquake to form plastic hinges and absorb energy. Generally, such eccentrically-braced frames (EBFs) have relied on the small-and-many philosophy and have been used only in smaller buildings with ductile links typically about 500 mm long.

Century Tower was the first building in a seismic area that Fosters had designed and they wanted to create a striking image to set it apart from the rest of the Tokyo skyline. For this building, Arups devised an entirely novel system of resisting earthquakes. It uses the EBF but, unlike Californian precedents, on a massive scale, spanning the full width of the building and two full-storey heights. For the first time, large column-free office floors were possible in an earthquake zone, and the large area of glazing in the façade is striking in comparison with other buildings in Tokyo.

In order to work effectively, such a structure had to be far more rigorously engineered than is usual in such buildings. Being totally unprecedented, and on such a large scale, the behaviour was very difficult to predict. Also, since the structure has far fewer members than other EBFs, it becomes essential that they all form plastic hinges in a severe earthquake, and exactly as intended. In a smaller building with many and smaller members, the occasional malfunction is tolerable.

The whole philosophy of the new design was incompatible with the traditional Japanese approach to the prob-

lem. It was recognised early on that a major effort would be needed to persuade the local regulatory authorities of the suitability of the design and that the approach to demonstrating its adequacy and safety, as used in California, would be appropriate in Japan. For instance, when using plastic design methods, the absolute magnitude of the loads on the building is less significant than the study of the possible collapse mechanisms, which can be investigated by a relatively simple analysis of a complex model of the whole structure, rather than by complex analysis of a simpler model. Also, in the proposed Century Tower it was not possible to avoid problems of torsion, again in contrast to established Japanese practice. This problem was largely solved by making the frames from box sections which are able to resist torsion without suffering the torsional instability of I-sections.

After selecting an EBF, the proportions of the frame had to be determined, a decision which depended largely on the length of the ductile link: a short link would fail in shear, while a long link would fail in bending. An optimum link length of 9 metres was selected. This also suited the architects' vision for the façade – a bold architectural statement of structural form with hints of the brush strokes of Japanese calligraphy.

On this last point, a number of interesting differences can be seen between details of the structure as it works for the engineer, and the architectural image presented in the finished building:

- the angle of the brace to the horizontal is not parallel to that of the aluminium honeycomb cladding that surrounds it;
- the axes of the structural members forming the K-brace pass through a single point to prevent rotation of the joints (the clad structure appears otherwise);
- the size of the box-section frames decreases from floor to floor up the building; the overcladding does not;
- the slenderness of the 125-mm tubular hangers which carry the suspended mezzanine floors is disguised by their 400-mm diameter cladding.

The innovative use of the large K-bracing in the east–west structural frames was not repeated in the orthogonal direction. It was found that it would

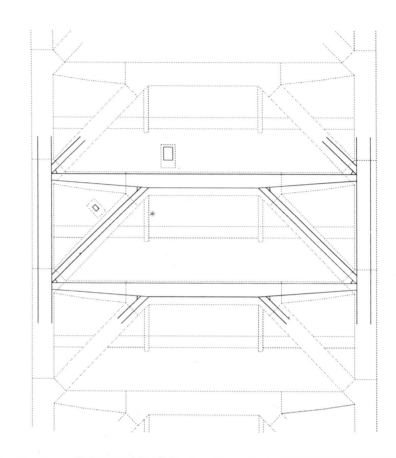

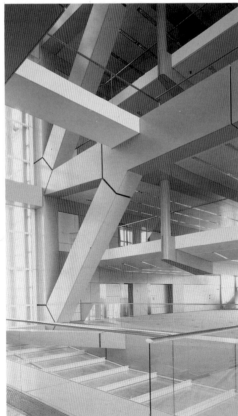

severely interfere with access between the services towers and the office floors. Instead, a conventional moment frame was used with many closely-spaced columns and beams. The result is a striking visual contrast between the two types of structural system.

Further reading

The Structural Engineer, Vol. 70 No. 18, 15 September 1992, pp. 313–317
Colin Davies and Ian Lambot, <u>Century Tower</u>, Watermark, 1992
<u>Architectural Review</u>, November 1992, pp. 27–37

Interaction

Building services consist of many networks conveying various 'fluids' (including electricity and information). 'Ducts' can vary considerably in size, both from one fluid to another, and from the start to finish of a distribution route. Building structure can be looked at in the same way – a network of elements conveying a variety of loads from their points of application to the foundations. The size of the 'ducts' (now load paths) can vary considerably from path to path and along their length. The two sets of networks interpenetrate and, by and large, compete for the same volumes, between the spaces used by the occupants. Interaction between structure and services is therefore unavoidable and it is convenient to look at this from two points of view: behaviourally and geometrically.

Behavioural interaction arises from the inevitable fact that any structural element in a building will have properties which may affect the control of the internal environment and the services installations, and *vice versa*. The thermal properties of structural elements are an obvious example: their heat capacity, coefficient of expansion, thermal inertia and how warm or cold they feel to the touch. A little less obvious are acoustic properties (reflection and absorption), electrical and electromagnetic properties (insulation, radio transparency), optical properties (transparency, surface texture and reflectivity), reaction to air-borne moisture, and so on. Conversely, building services will give rise to loads which need to be carried safely to the foundations: self-weight, vibrating loads from rotating machinery, reactive loads that occur as fluids are diverted around corners, loads arising from thermal movement of ducts and services installations, and so on.

The geometric interaction arises mainly from the need for structure and services routes to cross one another, especially in the space between one ceiling level and the floor level of the storey above.

Building designers have developed many ways of dealing with these different interactions. It is generally essential to agree how tightly integrated the structure and services are to be – kept separate in zones with a minimum of interference (flat slab with raised floor and suspended ceiling), or with various degrees of interpenetration (ducts in the voids between ribs or floor beams, pipes passing through the holes of a castellated beam, and so on).

With increasing concern for environmental matters and energy saving, the thermal and acoustic properties of concrete and masonry are being exploited more and more ingeniously. As with many developments in building design, the progress of recent centuries or decades has arisen not so much from inventions, but from an awareness of the principles underlying various phenomena already used in traditional buildings. Hence it is possible to devise ways of describing and thinking about such knowledge and be able to achieve results deliberately and with accuracy – by design.

Many earlier designers achieved an inventive interaction of structure and services – from Roman hypocausts and air-cooled mud buildings in hot climates to St George's Hall, Liverpool – but the modern approach was developed in Britain mainly by a few interdisciplinary practices designing increasingly highly-serviced buildings in the 1960s. Arup Associates deserve mention for the development of the 'tartan grid' as a way of structuring and formalising planning strategies, and of some of the first low-energy buildings, using concrete's thermal inertia to recycle heat.

It is always more satisfying to design the services in harmony with the architecture and the structure, so that they are not fighting one another. I almost feel the strain on the heating and air-conditioning of a building which has inappropriately been made with a steel frame and lightweight floors and cladding, rather than built of concrete and masonry. Both drains and foundations can make the construction of buildings very difficult and can lead to awkward differential movement problems.

I am continually puzzled why anyone needs persuading that services and structure must be integrated when a building is being designed. It may be that the integration, in a particular case, consists simply of agreeing that services and structure be kept apart. It is rarely so simple, but it is nearly always possible to find an economic structural system which gives the services engineers all they want by way of space, distribution routes, thermal properties – even acoustic. More difficult is the task of demonstrating to unenlightened clients, architects and engineers the benefits of doing so, despite the copious evidence that buildings will need to be reserviced many times before they are demolished.

Max Fordham

Bracken House

London 1991

Structural engineer   John Thornton, Rob Kinch
Ove Arup & Partners

Architect   Michael Hopkins & Partners
Client   Obayashi Europe BV

Bracken House was formerly the headquarters of the Financial Times. The new building retains the two end wings of the 1959 listed building but replaces the centre with a design rather closer in form to Guarini's Palazzo Carignano which had inspired the original design. No building is conceived in a vacuum, and design concepts pass from one project to another: old ideas and materials are revisited, new combinations are found. In Bracken House several themes used in the Mound Stand at Lord's cricket ground, on which engineers and architect had worked together, are re-used and developed further.

The proximity of St Paul's Cathedral meant severe height restrictions and called for particularly close integration of structure and services in order to reduce the height of each storey to 3.9 metres and so be able to incorporate six floors in the new central section of the building, rather than five. At the same time the architect wanted the façade to be part of the structure rather than a curtain wall.

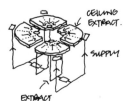

THE CONCEPT: WHEEL

STRUCTURAL ORGANISATION

FLOOR SERVICES SUPPLY BETWEEN STRUCTURE

EXTRACT

CEILING EXTRACT.

SUPPLY

Many different structural schemes were considered in the search for one which would provide a sufficiently thin floor sandwich – in-situ-concrete beams and slabs, precast-concrete beams, steel beams with concrete fire protection and vaulted slabs reminiscent of the brick jack-arches used in many 19th-century industrial buildings.

Inspired partly by the architectural scheme for the building outline, it was decided to impose a radial organisation to the services and structure and ensure that no large services needed to cross the line of the beams. Their lower surface could be left exposed, both to save the space lost above a false ceiling and to express the building's structural and services grid. This idea favoured the choice of precast-concrete beams which, as well as giving the high quality of finish required, would also help increase the speed of construction. The columns are of in-situ concrete.

The main services run in the void between the radial beams. In order to locate the supply air ducts and fans at floor level and the lighting units and

extract air plenum at ceiling level, the structural slab between radial beams is, unusually, set at about mid-depth of the beam. The depths of these beams was also reduced in two ways. They were placed relatively close together, both to reduce the area of floor each must carry and to match the grid of the retained part of the building. The span of the beams, and hence their depth, was also reduced by setting the outer columns 4.2 metres in from the façade and supporting the outer floor section as a cantilever propped by the façade.

Services are distributed perpendicular to the radial beams in two spaces. Small power and communication cables run in any direction in the void of the false floor above the beams. Large air-supply ducts run circumferentially from risers near the external façade in the space made by omitting the up-standing half of the cantilevered outer ends of the radial beams. Extracted air is taken down in the central core of the building.

Determining the length of the cantilever section of the radial beams was not a straightforward matter. In early schemes it was found that, wherever the outer column was placed along the length of the beam, either the load on the façade would be too great or there would be insufficient space available for the services in the outer circumferential zone. The final geometry was the result of many iterations and paring down dimensions millimetre by millimetre, and was strongly influenced by the performance requirements of the building in a severe fire.

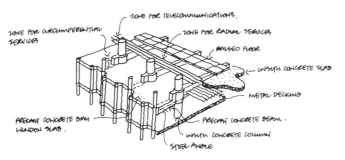

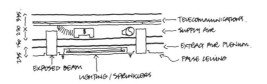

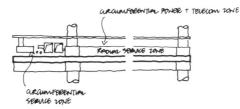

The structural façade itself is made of cast gun-metal, a type of bronze. The recessed columns prop the cantilevered section of the radial beams while outer, smaller columns support the portion of the floor slab that extends into the window bay. In extreme circumstances,

however, support by the exposed metal columns could not be relied upon.

The safety and integrity of the building structure in extreme circumstances was able to be justified using the reduced imposed loads and partial factors of safety allowable in the design codes. These take account of the fact that, during any fire which would damage the façade, people would leave the building and floor loadings would therefore be lower. Once it was ascertained that the façade structure need carry only the floor loads assumed for normal use, not when the building is unoccupied, a suitable position for the columns could then be found.

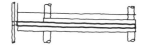

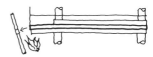

Further reading

Arup Journal, Vol. 27 No. 2, Summer 1992, pp. 3–7
Proceedings of the Institution of Civil Engineers: Structures and Buildings, Vol. 104 No. 2, May 1994, pp. 167–182
The Architects' Journal, 27 May 1992, pp. 26–41
Architectural Review, May 1992, pp. 26–39
Concrete Quarterly, No. 168, Spring 1991, pp. 12–15

Sama Bank buildings

Saudi Arabia 1978–81

Structural engineer	Tom Schollar
	F J Samuely & Partners
Services engineer	**Orsi & Koener**
Architect	**Brown Daltas Associates**
Client	**Sama Bank**

The interior of the bank gives an impression of great simplicity and, considering how highly-serviced it is, the building is strikingly uncluttered by ducts, risers and outlets. This effect was achieved by designing the services simultaneously with the building structure and creating a very high degree of integration.

To give a large column-free space, the four upper floors of the building are suspended from a space-truss roof, 4.6 metres deep, which spans 30 metres between the four supporting concrete towers. The loads in such a large truss are too high for the joints of proprietary space-truss systems and special node connections were designed to carry up to 1000 tonnes. The results of the computer modelling were checked using physical models and each node was individually proof-tested beyond its design load. The floors are suspended by steel-wire rope hangers, which are very thin compared with the corresponding size for columns acting in compression. The whole of the steel structure, including space-truss roof, floor beams and metal decking, is exposed; fire protection is achieved solely by active means, a solution which would not, at present, be allowed in Britain.

The floor beams are on a 3 x 3-metre grid and are all 700 mm deep to allow standard connections to be used with standard partitions fixed beneath them. All the services, including air ducts, are contained within the voids of the metal deck floor which, at 190 mm, is much deeper than is usual. By this means air is distributed through a very large number of ducts, which can thus be of reduced size. The sprinklers, power, telephones and lighting are also carried in the floor-deck voids. Dark anodised aluminium grilles hang below the lighting tubes, which are themselves recessed into the floor deck, and sprinkler heads identify the deck runs containing the sprinkler mains. Clearly, with such tight integration, there is virtually no possibility of changing the system in any future refurbishment.

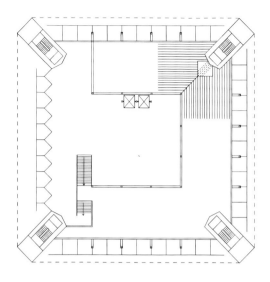

To achieve the best services distribution the metal deck was arranged in straight runs between the towers, where they pass through holes cast in the concrete wall. As the floors move relative to the towers, all services have flexible connections between the floor runs and the risers inside the towers. The corners of each floor plate presented a special problem as only part of the floor containing duct runs intersects with the tower. Here the metal deck was modified to enable the runs to turn through 45° in plan by passing under a solid-steel floor plate before entering the tower.

At the entrance to the building a massive glass wall and aluminium sun screen, 26.5 x 13.7 metres high, hang from the underside of the upper floor. The glass façade is a folded-plate structure, a form more often employed horizontally in roofs. It is a particularly effective way of using the glass to act both as the building envelope and as the structure to carry the substantial wind loads on the sun screen and glass back to the main load-bearing structural elements. The glass also serves to stabilise the sun screen, which is made from hundreds of 100 mm lengths of aluminium alloy extrusion dovetailed together, by hand, in jigsaw fashion. Unlike many more recent glass structures this one is not cluttered by a forest of struts and cables to provide the lateral stability.

Royal Exchange Theatre

Manchester 1976

Structural engineer	Ove Arup & Partners	Services engineer	Max Fordham & Partners
		Architect	Levitt Bernstein Associates
		Client	Royal Exchange Theatre Company

The location of this small theatre inside Manchester's old Cotton Exchange presented several unusual challenges: to devise a suitable structure, provide air conditioning for a building within a building, and ensure safety for both the audience and the structure in a fire.

As the old Exchange floor was judged unable to support the proposed new loads, the entire theatre is built on two transfer structures which carry loads to the centres of four existing, massive masonry columns. Steel was chosen to provide the lightest possible structure, but an inherent disadvantage of lightweight steel structures is that they suffer relatively large deflections and are very springy – they can vibrate easily and for a long time. A damping system had to be devised which would both permit the large deflection under static loads and ensure that a rowdy audience could not excite and reinforce vibrations at the structure's natural frequencies and, quite literally, bring the house down. A stability connection between the suspended theatre structure and the Corn Exchange floor was developed which would allow rotation and vertical movements of up to 65 mm: relative movement between the two was damped using pairs of modified shock absorbers made for heavy Ford trucks. (Connections with a similar potential for movement had to be incorporated in some of the air-conditioning ducts.)

The brief for the theatre required that no one in the audience of 700 should be further than 9 metres from the centre of the stage. This limited the number of people who could be seated on the ground floor and led to a need for two galleries. To ensure good visibility, these galleries had a very limited ceiling height, leaving very little space in which to fit adequate air conditioning and the supporting structure.

A solution was achieved by developing the air-distribution system simultaneously with the structural system. The result was an intimate integration of air paths and structural elements, often with air ducts shaped precisely to exploit voids created by the structure.

The provision of air conditioning in a building leads inevitably to a hierarchy of ventilation spaces, decreasing markedly from the air intake to the delivery points. In the theatre, this begins with the large air-handling plant, located in its own room to keep it acoustically separate from the auditorium. From there the main ducts fly up the outside of the structure to serve feeders which carry the air to opposite sides of the auditorium through the roof structure; these ducts are triangular in section, to make best use of the voids in the roof truss. From roof level the air paths drop down in wide, flat ducts and subdivide to serve each of the three seating levels.

With barely 2.4 metres between the gallery floors, a particularly ingenious solution was needed to squeeze both the air supply and outlet – and the steel frame and metal decking floor structure – into a depth of just 350 mm.

The air is first carried circumferentially beneath the gallery floor in flat ducts, 1500 mm wide and only 140 mm

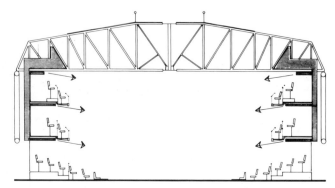

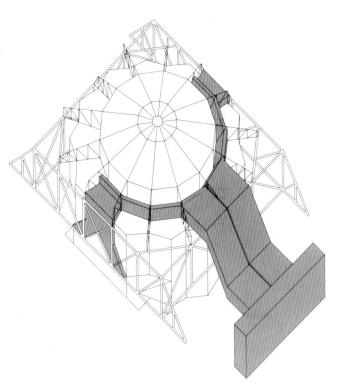

deep, which nestle under the cranked radial hollow-section beams that support the metal decking floor. At intervals around the gallery, holes in the top of this duct allow air to rise into the shallow void bounded by the gallery floor above, the circumferential duct below, and the two radial cranked ribs on each side. The choice of geometry for this duct was also influenced by its effectiveness in reducing turbulence in the air flow and so reducing noise which might be carried into the auditorium.

The air then flows radially inwards towards the auditorium, is diverted downwards past the step in the gallery floor above, and is then deflected again to the horizontal direction by the electrical trunking. This last space is effectively a duct with only three walls; the airflow is kept horizontal by a hydrodynamic effect (the Coanda effect). Just as a stream of water falling from a tap clings to the back of a spoon, so the airflow clings to the plate forming the top of this 'duct' and is carried clear of the edge beam into the auditorium.

In addition to its unusual structure and servicing, this theatre was remarkable for its time in being an all-steel structure. In the mid-1970s, intumescent paints were not of their present quality, and the prevailing practice was to avoid exposed steel on the grounds that it lost most of its strength in a fire. Since steel was essential to the project's viability, a concerted effort was made to provide a rational justification of the safety of both the audience and the structure in case of fire – an approach

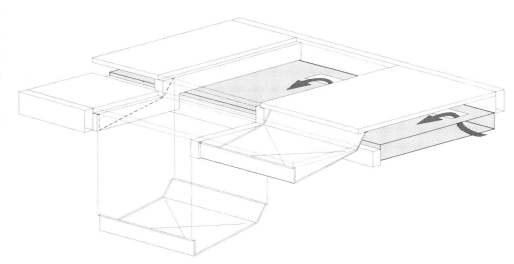

The cranked beams at the angles in the gallery are longer than elsewhere; adequate stiffness is achieved by using an I-section rather than RHS, and by using 45° stiffening webs at the cranks. These are more efficient than webs conceived as continuations of the flanges.

now generally known as fire engineering.

Rather than simply avoiding steel, a careful analysis was made of all the various consequences of a fire. Three arguments prevailed: by providing many exits, the audience could vacate both the theatre and the Exchange building quickly enough to avoid danger; even if a fire continued after evacuation, the collapse of the structure would not significantly affect either the Exchange building or the fire fighters; and finally, the likelihood of a fire taking place was reduced by selecting non-combustible or low-flammability materials. This fire-engineering approach was able to reas-

sure the local authorities that the structural steel could be used with no fire protection at all.

Further reading

Arup Journal, Vol. 11 No. 4, December 1976, pp. 18–23
The Structural Engineer, Vol. 56A No. 7, July 1978, pp. 189–197
Architectural Review, December 1976, pp. 356–362
The Architects' Journal, 28 January 1976, pp. 158–160

Lloyd's of London

Administrative Headquarters

Chatham 1978

Structural engineer <u>Arup Associates</u>

Architect <u>Arup Associates</u>

Client <u>Lloyd's of London</u>

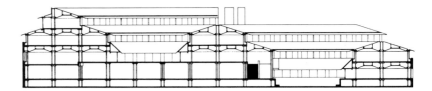

The popularity of air conditioning and the birth of office computing during the building boom of the late 1960s forced the industry to address the growing demands on space being made by building services. It was the decade in which many now familiar ideas were developed – the need for flexibility in office layouts, the need to allow services to be renewed without major intervention in the building structure, and the search for ways of reducing the cost of running buildings. It soon became clear that solutions to such problems demanded unprecedented close collaboration between the various members of the design team. 'Total design' and 'integration' became buzz words. It was during this decade that Arup Associates developed their uniquely intimate design teams as a means of addressing the complexity of a truly integrated design process. There was, in itself, little that could be called an invention, since structure and services have been interacting for centuries – the Roman hypocaust, even the domestic chimney breast. However, in the 1960s it was most unusual to focus on such issues in the design of a new commercial building, and the idea of energy conservation was almost unheard of. Many of the ideas developed by Arup Associates during that time are nowadays taken as standard.

It soon became clear, originally in a number of university research laboratories, that by developing architectural, structural and servicing ideas simultaneously, an entirely different sort of building was conceived. In particular, by

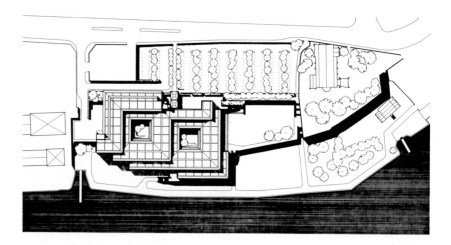

taking account of the interaction between structure and services new strategies arose. Both the geometric and the behavioral interaction could be controlled and put to mutual benefit: natural voids in structural systems could be exploited to house service runs, and structural concrete, with its high thermal inertia, could be used as part of the building's energy management system.

It also became clear that the consideration of so many interrelated and

competing demands and influences on a building's geometry was horrendously complex. It was found useful to condense many of these variables into a series of geometric grids which would impose a certain order and discipline on the otherwise infinite number of combinations. Four three-dimensional grids were used: the master grid, structural grid, services grid, and space-planning or partition grid. The relative sizes and spacing of these grids helped define volumes, areas and lines by which the different competitors for space might be constrained. The characteristic pattern which was thus formed led to its name, the tartan grid.

The administrative headquarters for Lloyd's of London at Chatham illustrates two of the more obvious consequences

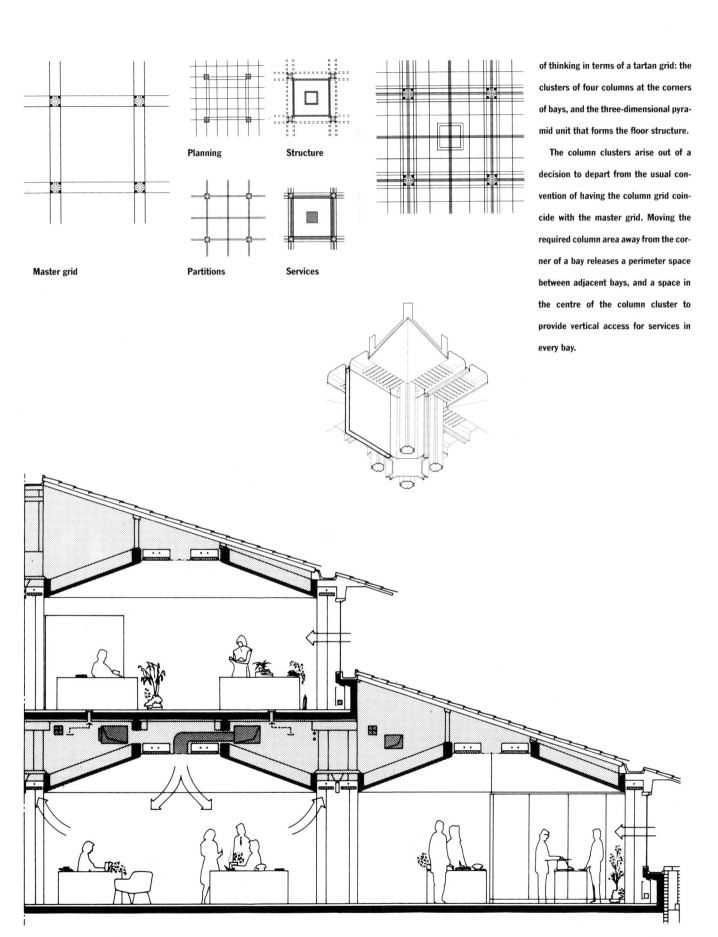

Master grid

Planning   **Structure**

Partitions   **Services**

of thinking in terms of a tartan grid: the clusters of four columns at the corners of bays, and the three-dimensional pyramid unit that forms the floor structure.

The column clusters arise out of a decision to depart from the usual convention of having the column grid coincide with the master grid. Moving the required column area away from the corner of a bay releases a perimeter space between adjacent bays, and a space in the centre of the column cluster to provide vertical access for services in every bay.

The pyramid floor units bring many advantages. From a purely structural point of view the pyramid is a truly three-dimensional (space) structure. It derives its strength and stiffness mainly from compression and tension actions rather than from bending, and thus needs less material. It is well suited to the use of precast concrete, and assembly becomes a rather cleaner and quicker process than the in-situ alternative. Adjacent precast units fit over bars protruding from the columns which are tied together by a precast link piece, and the assembly is then grouted to achieve structural integrity. Two hundred precast pyramids, each 7.2 metres square, were cast on site at the rate of one a day.

The pyramid unit provides an elegant separation of spaces at ceiling level. Rather than the ceiling void being entirely above the room space beneath, the two volumes interpenetrate one another so that a relatively large hidden void is available for services inside the volume, which the eye perceives as part of the office. This allowed the effective floor depth to be small compared with other structural systems while providing a services void large enough for a man to crawl through – a great asset when it comes to reservicing the building. The size and shape of the void were particularly useful in accommodating the large number of air ducts and other services: according to the partition layout, both lighting and air conditioning can be controlled locally in each quarter bay of the entire office area. The geometry of the pyramid also helped establish a suitable

airflow within the office space. Fresh air is introduced at the highest point in the centre of the bay and extracted from its circumference. From here it is drawn over the perimeter luminaires and takes away much of the heat these generate.

In various ways the three-dimensional structural grid introduces a hierarchy of spaces of different sizes and shapes within the master grid. These can be related closely to the services grids and the equivalent hierarchy of spaces they imply. Together the pyramids and column clusters serve to enhance the architectural qualities of the building interior and delineate a structured space beneath, without the need for partitions. By virtue of the lighting grid and the acoustic characteristics of each bay, a striking intimacy is brought to what would otherwise be a large and unbroken space.

Further reading

The Architects' Journal, 4 February 1981, pp. 199–217
Michael Brawne, Arup Associates, Lund Humphries, 1983

Haj Terminal

King Abdul Aziz International Airport

Jeddah 1980

Structural engineer	<u>Skidmore, Owings & Merrill</u>
Services engineer	<u>Skidmore, Owings & Merrill</u>
Architect	<u>Skidmore, Owings & Merrill</u>
Client	<u>Ministry of Defence and Aviation</u>

The terminal building at Jeddah is truly enormous. It needs to provide shelter for up to 80,000 pilgrims at a time – 1.5 million a year – waiting for periods of up to 36 hours, on their way to and from the holy city of Makkah. It covers an area of some 4.25 hectares and even today is still the largest fabric roof in existence.

Since the building is so large (note the relative size of the jumbo jets), ventilation had to be achieved mainly using natural convection. The conical shape of the tensile fabric roof structures was exploited to act as the means by which an updraught could be created. The structure itself thus became part of the services engineering. In addition to the natural stack effect of a chimney, cross winds blowing over the open top of the cones draws air up from below by virtue of lower pressure in the moving air. The precise shape of the roofs was developed after much testing of models in wind- and smoke-tunnels as well as the mod-

elling needed to determine a suitable shape from the structural point of view.

Rather surprisingly, the smoke-tunnel tests and analysis of air-flows and temperatures revealed that the air would be hotter near the ground than immediately beneath the roof fabric. Nine-metre tall ventilation columns were designed to create a forced-air circulation within the building itself. These take the cooler air from above and deliver it down to ground level. The columns were further exploited as multi-service units, housing both the up-lighting and the public-address system.

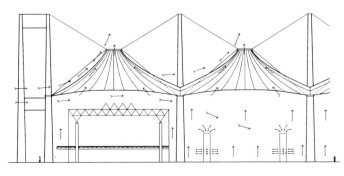

Further reading

<u>Civil Engineering (ACSE)</u>, Vol. 50
No. 12, December 1980, pp. 68–71

Westminster & Chelsea Hospital Roof

1992

Structural engineer <u>Buro Happold</u>

Architect <u>Sheppard Robson Limited</u>

Client <u>North West Thames Regional Health Authority</u>

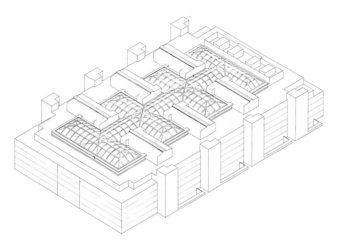

Glass is the usual choice for the transparent material of an atrium roof. However, it is heavy, especially if double glazing is needed to reduce heat losses, and a substantial structure is needed to give a glazed roof sufficient strength and stiffness. This is slightly paradoxical for a building element that is invisible and whose main function, after transparency, is to act as a barrier against heat and rain.

From time to time a project arises in which a variety of factors can suggest to engineer and architect a possible advantage in going back to first principles and analysing an old problem afresh. At the heart of the new Westminster & Chelsea Hospital is a vast barrel-vaulted atrium, 116 metres long and 85 metres wide, with four transepts. In view of the large area to be covered it seemed likely that recent developments in the field of lightweight structures might present some alternatives to the traditional glazing solutions.

The key to good thermal insulation in glazing is the air gap between the glass sheets. Transparent foils of plastic can

also be used to contain the air and are very much lighter but, alone, such a combination of materials has no useful structural properties. Here a lesson was drawn from the field of pneumatic structures: by inflating a flexible sheet it can be prestressed, and the combination of a tensioned sheet and compressed air can produce a structure with some useful rigidity.

These ideas were judged to be worth developing for this large atrium roof, especially in view of the high insulation that might be achieved. A transparent foil of the polymer ethylene tetra-fluoroethylene (ETFE) was found which had adequate tensile strength and resistance to tearing. To increase the thermal insulation it was decided to use three foils and it proved viable to create flat cushions of different shapes by clamping the foils at their edges and keeping them inflated by air maintained at slightly (0.5 per cent) above atmospheric pressure.

The size of the cushions was dictated by their ability to withstand wind and snow loads. The latter would be particu-

larly onerous, and if large panel sizes were to be achieved it became clear that an additional structural system would be needed. This took the form of a series of parallel stainless-steel wires beneath the cushions at 300-mm spacings, which would limit deflections under high loads and provide an additional load path back to the cushion supports. For easy construction it would also be necessary for the cushions to be pre-assembled as self-contained units which could be carried into position and fixed from the outside. The cushions that were developed in this way are about 4 metres x 3 metres in area and 250 mm thick at their centre. They have a thermal performance and transparency similar to triple glazing but at about one fiftieth of the weight.

The very low weight offers enormous potential to achieve both lightness and economy in the supporting structure. Both glass-reinforced plastic and aluminium alloy were considered as materials for making the arched supporting frames, and both have very much better strength-to-weight and stiffness-to-weight ratios than steel. Although the aluminium alternative was finally chosen for its low maintenance needs and superior durability, it also has a particular manufacturing advantage. Aluminium alloys can be formed into extremely complex cross-sections by extrusion through a die. This production technique enabled the many different functions of both the supporting frame for the foil cushions and the structural ribs of the barrel vault to be achieved using just two

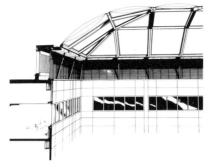

different extruded sections. The requirements were that the frame and ribs should:

- have a high section stiffness (second moment of area);
- support the stainless-steel wire grid;
- allow watertight fixing of the cushion foils into their frame;
- house the air-supply duct needed to inflate the foil cushions;
- incorporate an external gutter for rainwater;
- provide drainage channels for condensation forming in the box section;
- provide small drainage channels to catch condensation forming on the underside of the cushions;
- provide brackets for bolting together the various components and achieving waterproof joints;
- incorporate hooking points for internal cleaning gantries.

The new roofing system thus developed was not produced by taking an existing system and improving individual parts. There was a fundamental rethink as to how to achieve the required performance of an atrium roof. The result is a remarkably tight integration of structure and services: no one part can be changed without affecting some or all of the others – a singular solution for a unique set of circumstances.

It is interesting to note that the principles and logic behind this roofing system – developed by a very 20th-century approach to design and technology – are virtually identical to Paxton's glazed ridge-and-valley system which he developed for the Crystal Palace roof (except for the pneumatic element). But it is in the nature of any innovation, then, as now, that it is not possible to predict at the beginning of a project what the most suitable design will turn out to be. On this project, considerable time and effort for design development was needed in the early stages to achieve an original solution which would finally bring substantial benefits compared with conventional roofing systems. The risk in such an investment in resources is inversely proportional to the level of confidence in the skills of the design team.

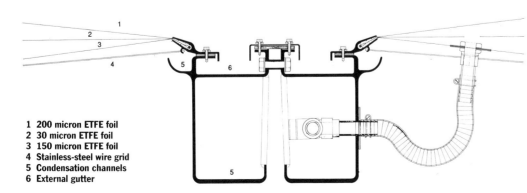

1 200 micron ETFE foil
2 30 micron ETFE foil
3 150 micron ETFE foil
4 Stainless-steel wire grid
5 Condensation channels
6 External gutter

Further reading

Structural Engineering International, Vol. 4 No. 1, February 1994, pp. 14–16

School of Engineering and Manufacture

De Montfort University, Leicester 1993

Structural engineer	**Martin Cranidge**
	<u>**YRM–Anthony Hunt Associates**</u>
Services engineer	**Edith Blennerhassett,**
	<u>**Max Fordham Associates**</u>
Architect	<u>**Short Ford & Associates**</u>

In a world where commercial buildings are often marketed on the strength of their performance, rather like cars, it is scarcely surprising that there is a perception that 'more is better'. Consequently, we have arrived at the lunatic position where many floors in buildings are capable of supporting loads three or four times larger than it is possible to place upon them, and air conditioning has become ubiquitous in a climate that hardly ever needs it. In the case of air conditioning the story has been aggravated by the fact that consultants and contractors clearly earn more money if there is more equipment to design and install.

The clients for the new School of Engineering and Manufacture wanted an innovative building, and this would not have been possible with traditional attitudes to building design and procurement. They wanted to create a building which would display the state of the art in environmental awareness, making the best use of natural heating, ventilation and lighting, and traditional construction materials. This required a radical approach to design by the architect and the services and structural engineers – especially the services design consultant who would, in effect, be paid to exclude as many services installations as possible; hardly an approach which a specialist contractor would take. By investing money at the design stage the client has obtained a low-cost building with particularly low running costs.

While the principles behind the design of the building are the same as

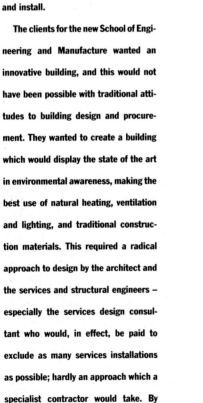

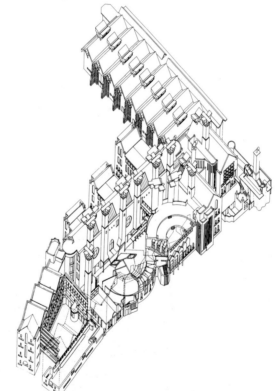

those underlying a Victorian building, they are executed on a massive scale. This required a late-20th-century understanding of the interaction between structure and services – complex three-dimensional load paths, the reinforcement of highly fenestrated masonry façades, differential movements between many materials, air flow

through purpose-designed voids in the structure, and the thermal performance of structural materials. Most particularly, the building design arises not from using a certain sort of structure, or method of servicing or materials technology, but from an attitude to the entire design by every person involved. The philosophy of environmental awareness permeates every aspect of the building, down, almost literally, to the last brick, nut and bolt or pane of glass, and to every area and volume of solid and void throughout an extremely complex three-dimensional geometry. A few examples can hardly do justice to the comprehensive originality of this building.

The design of the building is influenced mainly by the requirements for ventilation and cooling – in many areas the occupants and equipment generate sufficient heat to warm the building, even in winter. The structural and services systems are combined and work entirely passively.

Airflow through the deep-plan parts of the building is generated by the stack effect, a principle well tried in domestic chimneys and in many Arabic buildings in hot climates – warm air at the top of a ventilation duct rises and draws air in at the bottom. In summer the process works on a 24-hour cycle: during the day people and equipment heat the air which then rises up the ventilation ducts. This flow is improved by the design of the exposed tops of the ducts, which are covered with materials to absorb heat from the sun and encourage the stack effect. The ducts are also designed to exploit any cross-winds by channelling the wind to reduce the static air pressure and so draw air up the stack (the effect Bunsen used in his burner). Also, during the day, some of the heat generated within the building is removed as it heats up the fabric of the building. At night the process is reversed. Warm air continues to cycle through the building, drawing in the cool night air over the warm building fabric and removing the heat stored therein. This heat exchange is precisely controlled by regulating the airflow to pre-cool the building just enough to balance the temperature rise it will experience on the following day.

For this system to work it was essential that the materials used for the building structure would absorb sufficient heat and that good heat exchange between the structure and air would be achieved. A great many detailed studies were done to investigate the thermal performance of different designs and to

establish just what airflows and thermal mass the structure would need to discharge its function as a thermal moderator. The result is a large amount of exposed brick and blockwork for walls, and exposed ceilings of either precast-, prestressed-concrete double-T beams or in-situ slabs.

The ventilation ducts are themselves of load-bearing brickwork and are integral to the rest of the building structure. Since they are not needed right down to

ground-floor level, additional useful space was created by supporting them on single, steel columns which branch to support each corner of the diamond- or rectangular-section ducts.

The external walls are perforated by various air intakes to establish precisely the required airflow through the building. As well as having to be integrated into the structure and façade, the intakes needed an acoustic lining to prevent too much noise entering the building – and steel mesh to keep most of the wildlife out.

The walls of the double-height mechanical laboratory needed more substantial lateral restraint than normal because they support a travelling crane. The brickwork structures which buttress the wall are unusual in that they are hollow and act as air ducts. Part of their face is perforated to serve as the air intake.

The ventilation of the circular toilet

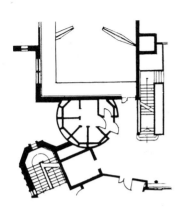

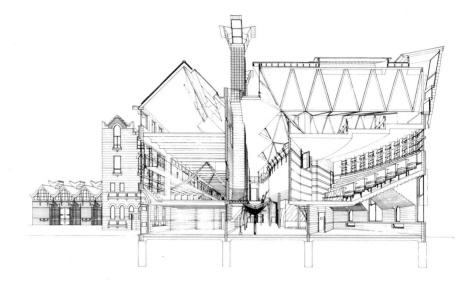

stacks at either end of the central block is on a smaller scale. Independent ventilation is provided from each WC on each floor up to roof level through ducts formed by the void of the double-skin masonry wall.

The requirement for natural daylight also had a direct impact on the structure – large areas of window are needed, often leaving too little masonry to be stable. In the electrical laboratory the load-bearing blockwork had to be reinforced with rods rather like reinforced concrete. Additional stability was pro-

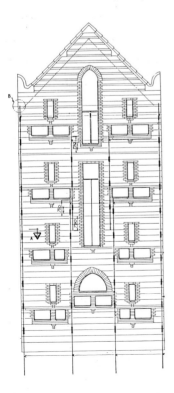

vided around highly-stressed openings by flat reinforcement in the joints between courses of blockwork.

At several places in the buildings daylight is brought through large holes in floors or internal load-bearing walls of upper storeys to illuminate the interior of large ground-floor spaces. In the general laboratory space, for instance, daylight and extract-ventilation is provided by holes so large their edges need their own support. Cranked struts were used to avoid an access walkway and the cruciform sections are fabricated from steel. Their varying cross-section reflects the bending they must resist; they are stabilised by light ties between their knees. The slender, brickwork mullions in the double-storey windows of this room are strengthened by vertical fish-belly Vierendeel girders.

With so many inter-penetrating volumes, both on plan and section, it was not always easy to achieve direct load paths through the building, or to provide enough shear walls to ensure adequate stability. In both the electrical and mechanical laboratories, stability is provided by the end walls, and wind loads are conducted to them through the pitched roofs. These are formed by two in-plane Warren trusses, joined along

their edges so that they can work by folded-plate action.

In the central building the complex internal geometry and lack of a convenient core prevented such a straightforward means of providing stability.

Shear walls shown by double lines

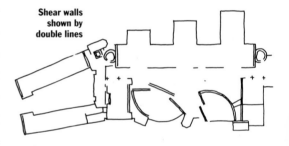

Sufficient resistance to shear had to be provided by a large number of flat and curved vertical surfaces, tied together by the floor screeds and the in-situ-concrete raked floors of the two main auditoria.

The net result is a highly innovative, low-energy building in which, at nearly every turn, the services and structure are working together, often with the same elements serving both systems.

Further reading

Architecture Today, No. 41, September 1993
Building Services, Vol. 15 No. 10, October 1993, pp. 20–25
The Architects' Journal, 9 March 1994, pp. 27–29

Form

Form and structure are inseparable – without structure there is no form; without form there is no structure. It is remarkable how a given amount of material, used in different ways, with different forms, can have such different structural characteristics.

Take a sheet of paper and put a crease in it: it gains stiffness and strength. Repeat many times and you have origami, the art of folded-plate structures.

Take a sheet of paper and curve it as an arch: it gains stiffness and strength. Continue the process and make a tube. On end it can now carry the weight of a brick. But it keeps untwisting and collapsing. Stick the free edge down with tape to form a closed tube and it becomes even stronger – it can now resist torsion.

Take a sheet of paper, cut out a circle and cut along a radius; form a cone and tape along the edge: it gains stiffness and strength. It does this by spreading into the third dimension and being restrained from falling back again into the flat world.

All these miracles of structure arise purely from form. Additional material is not the only way of enhancing structural properties, and seldom the most elegant.

In form we also have the void which, after all, is how structures become of use to the architect. The void can have quality as well as quantity.

In form we have the opportunity for deception for we have the means of making a structure look lighter without using less material. The heavy, static forms of Egyptian figure sculptures arise out of their form content, not their greater weight. Greek figures achieve their sense of lightness and movement by body posture, tension in muscles, folds in garments. In buildings, a piece of structure looks lighter if it is made from small or thin sections, dispersed as much as possible even though it will occupy a greater space – compare a roof truss with the alternative portal structure.

Civilisation's great form-makers – engineers, architects and sculptors – are both united and divided by their different attitudes to form, yet in the final instance they can realise their own visions only by integrating all three approaches in their form-making.

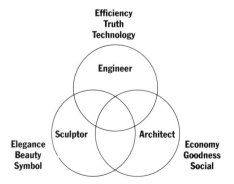

Bus station

Chur, Switzerland 1992

Structural engineer for roof	Peter Rice, Alastair Hughes – Ove Arup & Partners	Consulting engineer	Edy Toscano AG, Hegland & Partner AG
Consultant for glazing	RFR	Architect	Richard Brosi, Robert Obrist
		Lead client	PTT Switzerland

The principal requirement for the roof over the combined bus and rail station at Chur was transparency, both out of respect for the existing 19th-century station buildings and to ensure that the view of the surrounding mountains was not obscured.

A weatherproof and entirely transparent building envelope has been an ideal to strive for since the first large glass walls in Gothic cathedrals. The challenge has always been to reduce the visual impact of the metal supporting structure which any large area of glazing needs. Victorian glass houses undoubtedly got very near the limit, but spans were always small and the imposed loads they had to be designed to withstand were much lower than are required nowadays.

To span 52 metres and at the same time provide a delicate steel structure to give the building stability and enable it to withstand large and possibly asymmetric snow loading, required considerable ingenuity and the full power of modern computer modelling of the structural behaviour. The three-dimen-

sional geometry was often complex and a very high level of accuracy was often essential – all the fixings for the glazing, for instance, had to be positioned to within ±4 mm. To carry out these calculations manually would have been both tedious and labour intensive. Fast computers and three-dimensional CAD soft-

ware were essential to achieve the necessary geometrical accuracy economically; without them the roof and glazing would not have been executed as built.

Each of the twelve 'lemon-slice' (Zitronenschnitz) trusses is formed from a pair of tied, inclined, tubular arches and has a striking visual focus in the cast-steel joint which connects sixteen tie-rods at various angles. The arch tubes are linked by a regular welded grid of tubular purlins which act together effectively to form a Vierendeel lattice or grid shell and give the roof its longitudinal stability.

The decision was taken to keep the glazing and its supporting structure in two separate and parallel planes, linked only by the short radial tubes that support the stainless-steel glazing bars. The contrast between glazing and structure is further emphasised by running the glazing bars only circumferentially; longitudinal joints are of silicone. Above the glazing there is a further layer; thirteen longitudinal rails serve to support the cleaning gantry and to prevent snow sliding down onto hapless pedestrians.

In order to allow good access and circulation at the sides of the building, the roof trusses are suspended in pairs from twin columns, which themselves cantilever from the foundations so that both lateral and longitudinal stability is achieved without the need for crossbracing.

Being a semi-outdoor building, few services are required, but so sparse is the roof structure that even a few electrical conduits would have impaired its purity. The lighting for the entire bus station ingeniously avoids this problem. Clusters of convex mirrors are suspended high up and lit by spotlights mounted on the columns just above eye-level at the side of the building.

Further reading

Arup Journal, Vol. 28 No. 21, 1993, pp. 3–7
Werk, Bauen + Wohnen, No. 11, November 1993, pp. 28–35

Three roof forms

Structural engineer   Price & Myers

Architect   Nicholas Hare Architects

Felsted School Dining Hall

Client   Felsted School

Suffolk 1989

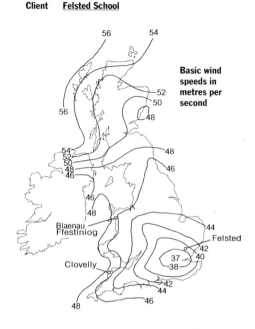

Basic wind speeds in metres per second

The form of roof trusses is influenced by both the architectural design and the loads which they must withstand – the weight of roof covering and wind forces. Wind flowing over a roof causes suction on the leeward slope which can result in considerable uplift on the whole roof structure. The uplift varies with the roof pitch, the building's geographical location and any sheltering it may receive from adjacent buildings. The influence of these loads can be seen in the structure and its form at every level – from the overall roof geometry, the choice of materials, the cross-section of the members, the method and geometry of connections between the members, down to the surface finish left after the manufacture and fabrication of the elements.

Basic wind speed	39 m/s
Exposure	sheltered (among buildings in open country)
Pitch	42°
Roof dead load	0.80 kN/m²
Maximum suction	-0.80 kN/m²
Net uplift	nil

A school hall needs to have a presence, and is traditionally a place of quality. The architects wanted to bring as much light as possible into the centre of the room and achieved this by means of a steep pitch with large triangular dormer windows and a warm timber ceiling to reflect the light. The dormer influenced the choice of 6 metres between trusses, but this resulted in an area of roof too great to support elegantly with a timber structure. Instead, a visually lighter-weight structure was created in steel using a combination of hollow sections and rods.

As the building is subject to relatively low wind loads, the steep roof pitch does not lead to excessive horizontal forces on the walls, and the uplift from the wind is never greater than the weight of the roof. The elements of the roof trusses normally acting in tension are, therefore, never subject to load reversal and could be made of very thin rods. The trusses were assembled and adjusted at the tie-rod ends, hidden inside a cylindrical junction box welded to the hollow-section steel strut.

Further reading

The Architects' Journal, 7 February 1990, pp. 36–43

	Structural Engineer	Price & Myers		Architect	Van Heyningen and Haward

Clovelly Visitors' Centre

Devon 1988

			Client	Clovelly Estate Co Ltd

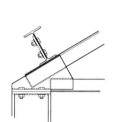

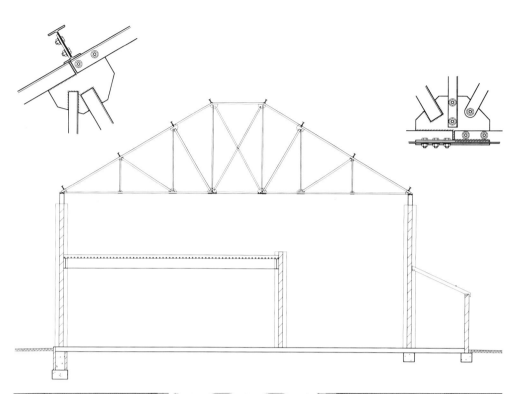

This building is on an exposed site in Devon and subject to very strong prevailing winds. It also has a low-pitched overhanging roof and stands on a cliff top, both of which factors accentuate the effect of the wind.

As the total uplift on this roof can be equivalent to <u>twice</u> its weight, a form of truss had to be found which would, effectively, work equally well upside-down! The purlins are very highly loaded and all the members of the trusses must be able to act as ties in tension and as struts in compression. The architects' wish for a straightforward steel structure was satisfied by a conventional truss made of welded angles and ties which give a sturdy and economical feel to the roof.

Further reading

<u>The Architects' Journal</u>, 31 May 1989, pp. 39–60
<u>Architectural Review</u>, May 1989, pp. 67–69

Basic wind speed	48 m/s
Exposure	high (cliff edge)
Pitch	30°
Roof dead load	0.7 kN/m²
Maximum suction	-1.4 kN/m²
Net uplift	-0.7 kN/m²

Blaenau Ffestiniog Sports Hall

Gwynedd, Wales 1989

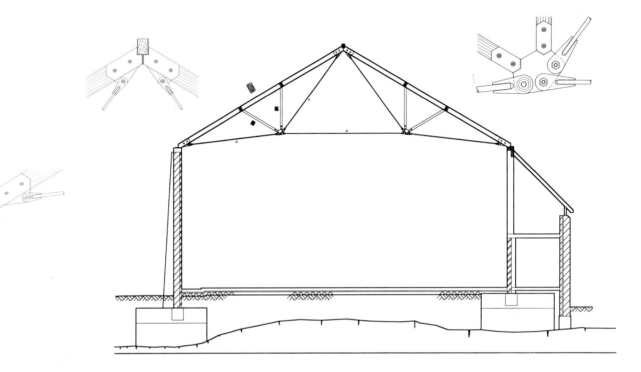

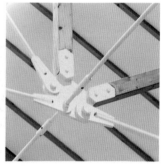

A sports hall is necessarily a plain box because of its function. Here the continuous rooflight provides even illumination and the main visual interest is the roof structure. The architect wanted to use timber where possible and appropriate; the purlins and all the compression members are therefore made of glued laminated timber. The ties and connections are of steel.

The building is subject to quite strong winds and the low pitch leads to relatively high uplift forces on the roof – greater, in fact, than the weight of the roof. In these circumstances the Glulam rafters resist the uplift loads by bending in the opposite direction from normal. There is, however, a complication: the uplift loads also tend to pull the walls together and the slender, steel tie-rods of the trusses are unable to act as struts to resist this. These forces and the lateral wind loads on the building are carried by the buttresses to the walls, which

are constructed as cantilevers held firm by the foundations.

The roof structure was made to look considerably lighter by choosing a form for the joints which would express the different material properties of steel and timber (their strengths and their different methods of connection).

A particularly nice detail is the welded joint between the circular tie-rod and the plate which bolts it to the main connection. The eye is drawn to a small D-

Basic wind speed	46 m/s
Exposure	medium (in a small town)
Pitch	30°
Roof dead load	0.75 kN/m²
Maximum suction	-0.85 kN/m²
Net uplift	-0.10 kN/m²

shaped hole which not only assists manufacture, but also forms a large radius of curvature in the notch in the steel plate and thus minimises any stress concentration. This is an effective way of preventing cracks and is especially important in the vicinity of joints where the steel may have been rendered brittle by the welding process.

Further reading

The Architects' Journal, 20 September 1989, pp. 40–47

Channel 4
Headquarters Building

London 1994

Structural engineer   Chris Wise, Adrian Falconer, Laurence Vye, John White <u>Ove Arup & Partners</u>

Architect   <u>Richard Rogers & Partners</u>

Specialist glazing contractor   <u>Eiffel, Permasteelisa (UK)</u>

Client   <u>Channel 4</u>

When approaching the entrance to this building, architect and engineer are likely to be struck by the same two features, but perhaps in different ways as a result of their respective perception of form.

To the left of the entrance is a stack of four conference rooms supported by bold, fabricated steel columns and floor beams which meet at pronounced structural pin-joints. The engineer's eye is likely then to look for further means of support since the structure, as it appears, is a mechanism and unstable. Lateral restraint for the stack is, in fact, inherent in the floor plates which can-

tilever out from the main body of the building and act as a horizontal shear structure. The exception is at roof level where a small brace renders the pin-joint rigid and transforms the top storey into a portal frame.

Although there are more obvious ways of stabilising the frame – with

cross-bracing or a Vierendeel frame – these would not have created such a vivid architectural and engineering effect.

The main entrance to the building is situated at the base of a 20-metre-high glass wall. This is particularly striking for two reasons: it is made of curved glass plates and appears to lack any means of support. Rather than a vertical structure of steel rods from which the glass panels are hung – the method which has become the norm in glass façades – the glass itself forms part of the load-bearing structure. Each panel is 12 mm thick, measures up to 3 metres x 2.1 metres, and carries the weight of all the panels below.

The entire weight of the glass wall is supported at roof level by three groups of fingers that cantilever off the roof. The engineer wanted the form of the struts in these cantilever structures to reflect their structural function and the way they resist failure by buckling. By fabricating them from steel plate it was possible to create a varying section stiffness (second moment of area) corresponding to the bending resistance which different cross-sections must be able to develop along the length of the strut.

As a geometric form, a third of a cylinder is easy enough to imagine and is a powerful means of focusing attention on the entrance; the idea is not uncommon. But to construct it out of glass is a bold architectural statement and was an intensely complex engineering achievement – made possible only by close collaboration between the architects,

structural engineers and specialist contractors who devised and installed the glazing system. Much of the complexity arose from the fact that the façade is not simply a third of a circle on plan; it also has glass returns at either side. This gives the dramatic effect of the whole foyer area appearing to project out from the concrete-frame building, despite the fact that it is contained in the re-entrant angle between the two main blocks. However, such a projecting façade is far more difficult to support than a glass wall which spans between two parts of a building which can provide firm anchorages.

The glass façade is suspended from sprung supports at roof level. Each panel hangs from the one above by stainless-steel castings at each corner. These also link each panel to its horizontal neighbours. Should one panel fail, shock loads are dissipated by the sprung supports and the weight of the panels below is carried by neighbouring panels, partly by the corner joints and partly by shear in the silicone sealant between the panels.

Alone, however, a series of suspended glass sheets could not withstand wind forces and some means of lateral restraint is necessary. To emphasise the transparency of the wall the bracing structure would need to be located entirely within the narrow foyer and be as visually lightweight as possible.

The challenge was to provide a grid of points, rigidly fixed in space, adjacent to each of the cast-steel brackets and roughly equidistant from them. Since the member connecting the glass to the sta-

bilising structure would have to carry both tension and compression, it could not be a cable. It would have been possible to devise a cable-and-strut scheme to provide the necessary stability, but some of the struts would have needed to be very long, and correspondingly bulky, to prevent buckling.

A prestressed cable-net scheme was proposed which avoided the need for all but very short struts. Horizontal cables following the curve of the glass could be kept taut by a series of vertical cables curved in the opposite sense. In principle this idea was simple enough and, since the steel would be used in tension, the amount of material in the bracing structure could be kept to a minimum. There was just one, rather serious, difficulty: the glass walls that form the returns were at the very places where the horizontal cables might be attached to the building.

In order that the grid of fixed points

could follow the glass surface around the corner at the returns and back to a firm anchor on the main building, the horizontal cables of the cable-net would need to reverse their curvature in the vicinity of the returns. Being a pre-stressed cable-net, this would entail the vertical cables near the returns passing outside the horizontal cables, adjacent to the glass. In the horizontal plane, these corner cables provide the restraint against which all the other cables are stressed – they have the largest section and curve between floor and ceiling in the opposite sense (inwards) to the vertical cables in the centre of the glass wall.

The complete cable-net consists of seven cables in the vertical plane, pre-

stressed by an orthogonal grid of eight horizontal cables. Perhaps its most striking feature is the large difference in thickness between the horizontal and vertical cables. This arises out of the very way in which a cable-net works as a structure. Its out-of-plane stiffness (perpendicular to the glass) depends on the degree to which the cables are prestressed against one another. This in turn depends on two factors: the forces in the cables and their curvature. A certain stiffness can be achieved using a high curvature and small cable tension, or low curvature and high tension. As the radius of curvature of the horizontal cables is typically about 6 metres and so they can be small (between 9 and 11 mm in diameter). The vertical cables have a radius of curvature of about 70 metres and need to be much larger (up to 40 mm) to carry tensions of up to 44 tonnes. They are, nevertheless, loaded well below their capacity of 130 tonnes; this gives ample reserve to prevent any possibility of a fatigue failure resulting from varying wind loads on the façade.

There remained the problem of how to stabilise the free edge at the junction between the curved glass surface and the flat return. After considering a variety of cable and strut restraints, it was finally achieved by exploiting the strut-assisted folded-plate action of the two glass planes: shear forces are carried between the two planes by the silicone sealant.

Further reading

Peter Rice and Hugh Dutton, <u>Le Verre Structurel</u>, Editions du Moniteur, 1990
<u>The Architects' Journal</u>, 20 April 1994, pp. 29–39

Link walkway

Manchester Airport 1993

Structural engineer	Travers Morgan
Lead consultant/designer	David Tasker, Travers Morgan
Electrical engineer	Travers Morgan
Mechanical engineer	Aukett

'Only connect' might well have been the brief for this passenger link between two airport buildings. A structure was needed which had a clear and stylish presence, but which did not compete with the striking buildings at each end. The challenge was to create a bridge which looked more like a building and appeared not to weigh heavily on the ground. It also had to be designed and built in thirteen months over roads which are in use 24 hours a day, a tight schedule which was achieved largely through the close co-operation possible in a construction management contract.

Architect   **Aukett**

Construction management   **Taylor Woodrow**

Client   **Manchester Airport**

The result is simple, elegant and, one might even say, obvious. But these characteristics of good design are deceptive and the end results alone can tend to render invisible the effort and skill which went into the process.

Between supports 30 metres apart, the structure has to be unusually stiff. The moving walkways can tolerate a deflection of only one thousandth of the span (compared, typically, with one three hundredth in buildings). The main structural members are deep steel beams welded from 54 mm x 980 mm steel plate and provide a backbone for the transverse floor ribs. These in turn support the curved two-pin arch ribs on which is hung the cladding that forms the tube. Wind loading on the tube is carried back to the bridge piers by thin concrete floor decks working in shear which run either side of the moving walkway. The bridge is given torsional stiffness by regular shear links between the two main beams which create what is effectively a perforated box girder.

The bridge piers are wider in elevation at the top than at ground level. This creates the important effect of visually detaching the bridge from the ground and making it seem to float – an effect suggestive of animals' legs perhaps rather than of trees or most columns, which taper the other way. In fact, there is also a good technical reason for this taper. The columns need to be wider at the top to reduce the stress levels where they pick up the large point load from the bridge girders; the loads are distributed over a larger area at ground level.

To preserve the clean line of the passenger tube the main services are all squeezed into the small space alongside and beneath the moving walkway. This is achieved by several means – the size of the largest air duct is reduced by using several small pumps situated along the length of the bridge rather than one large one; the air ducts pass through the transverse structural ribs; the air is introduced and removed through a small slot between the floor and glazing; the only access to the main services is from below, as in an aircraft. The remaining services – lighting, secondary cabling, smoke detection and extraction, closed-circuit television and communication links – are contained in a longitudinal ribbon suspended from the ceiling, again reminiscent of the suspended pods used in wide-bodied aircraft.

And, as a particularly elegant integration of structure and services, the reinforcement bars in the bridge piers serve as lightning conductors.

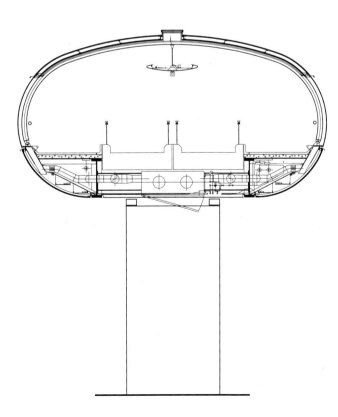

Further reading

New Steel Construction, August 1993, pp. 25–27
The Architects' Journal, 17 November 1993, p. 15

Lowara Offices

Vicenza, Italy 1985

Structural engineer   <u>Studio d'ingegneria: Favero – Milan</u>

Architect   <u>Renzo Piano</u>

Client   <u>Lowara-Montecchio Magiore</u>

As a manufacturer of pumps, the client wanted a building which displayed excellence in engineering design as well as high-quality architecture. Right from its earliest stages, the essential architectural features of the building – an office to house 150–200 employees in a single, large open space – were established. This apparently simple task was rendered rather more challenging by the fact that costs had to be kept well below the market average. The aim became to achieve 'perfect office accommodation, but made of nothing'.

The Lowara building is a light and minimal technological container. A few simple planning propositions gave rise to the idea of a prefabricated structure in steel which could be used most efficiently by ensuring that the building components were designed above all for exposure to axial stress. The use of steel in its simplest and most elementary forms came to represent a kind of motif

for the project, whose various features are linked both structurally and aesthetically by a common logic of essentiality and simplicity.

The roof is 150 metres long and suspended from two supports, at different levels and 15 metres apart. This concept was relatively easy to imagine as a structural principle. However, turning this simple idea into a buildable structure which could resist the many different loading configurations required much development and relied heavily on complex computer analysis of wind loads and deflections of the roof. The precise geometrical configuration derived from several considerations, each corresponding to certain loading conditions. The catenary shape reflects the action of the roof's dead weight; the parabola, the uniformly distributed loads, a circular arch form would be the easiest to construct. The roof also had to withstand asymmetric loading due to wind.

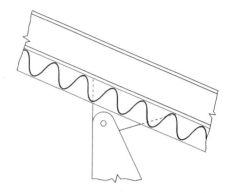

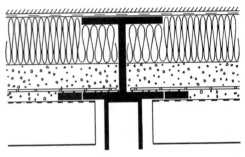

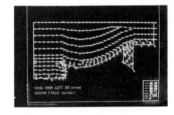

Air-flow simulation

Air-pressure simulation

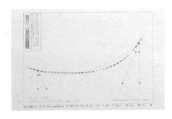

Deflection due to wind

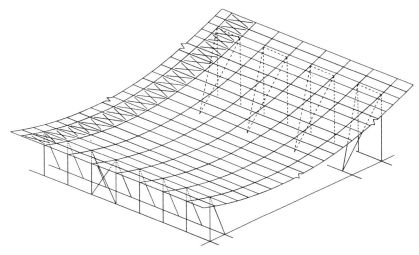

The final form of the concave surface is bi-parabolic and asymmetric with respect to its lowest point, a shape which, in fact, deviates only slightly from a true catenary curve. With extensive iterative analysis it was possible to reduce bending in the roof to a minimum and squeeze the seven separate layers into a total thickness of just 156 mm.

Longitudinal stability of the structure is provided in three ways. On the north (lower) side the ribs are supported from bipods arranged in the vertical plane at 3-metre centres. These are stabilised longitudinally by cross braces in three bays. The rear trestles are higher and consist of pairs of diverging struts every 6 metres – an arrangement which is self-stabilising. In the plane of the roof the fifty shaped ribs are stabilised by corrugated sheets welded to the intrados. These sheets are extremely thin (1.6 mm) and the necessary rigidity and structural resistance was achieved by using particularly deep corrugations (56 mm).

The vertical tie-down elements of each of the front trestles also support the external frame which carries the main glass façade. Delicate constructions of this kind are inherently subject to large deformations and the glass in the front façade had to be protected from stress by inserting a flexible plate element in polycarbonate above the glass panes.

The foundations, an element which is normally concealed, are raised to the level of the finished flooring where they provide fixings for the bipods. Although these concrete plinths are a structural necessity, the architect was able to use them as decorative elements in the floor.

Further reading

Architectural Review, September 1987, pp. 72–76
Architecture and Urbanism (extra edition – Renzo Piano), 1989, pp. 89–95
Proceedings of XIII Congress of C.T.A. (Collegio dei Tecnici dell'Acciaio), October 1991, pp. 203–212

Norwich Sport Village

1987

Structural engineer <u>Heinz Isler</u>

Architect <u>Copeland Associates</u>
in conjunction with
<u>Haus & Herd</u>

During the last quarter of a century, perhaps for the first time in about two thousand years, virtually no compression roof structures have been built. Roman domes and barrel vaults, Gothic vaults and baroque domes (and their copies) were ubiquitous until well into this century. From the 1940s, reinforced concrete in the form of a variety of thin shells was able to continue the tradition, using both a new material and developments in engineering science which enabled the behaviour and stability of such shells to be confirmed and justified. The bold displays by Maillart, Candela, Nervi and Torroja (engineers all) of what could be achieved with concrete shells might well have been the inspiration in the late 1950s for Utzøn (an architect) to propose his Sydney Opera House. Unfortunately, the shape of the roof he imagined was not suitable to work as a structural thin shell: the roof would need to develop significant bend-

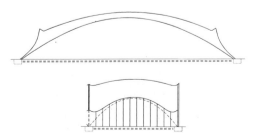

ing moments to withstand gravity and wind loads. It required an unprecedented onslaught by highly skilled and mathematically-talented engineers from Ove Arup & Partners, using the recently developed electronic computer, to make the scheme work at all – by disguising a stiff folded-plate structure beneath a smooth exterior. Nevertheless, this project progressed the understanding of shell behaviour substantially and for a decade or so many more such structures were built. Since the 1970s, however, they have largely fallen out of favour; the labour- and material-intensive process of casting in-situ concrete is usually said to be to blame. The need for above-average mathematical skills might have contributed too.

Meanwhile, in Switzerland, Heinz Isler continued to develop and build concrete shells as if he had not heard they were no longer in fashion. He took a highly experimental approach, drawing upon physical analogues to create his forms, in particular Hooke's observation that a hanging chain or net would, if inverted, form a stable compression arch, vault or

dome. Gaudí had used such models in the 1890s to develop the form of the vaults for his cathedral of the Sagrada Familia in Barcelona. More recently Frei Otto and others at the Institute for Lightweight Structures in Stuttgart have experimented with hanging nets in their search for structures which find their own form, and used these to devise appropriate shapes for compression timber grid-shells.

Isler came upon the shapes made by hanging fabrics rather by chance. Although he found them attractive, in themselves, he also realised that, when inverted, they could offer a means of

Client   IHS Sport Villages plc/
Broadland District Council
Joint Venture

creating the form of a compression shell. He did some simple experiments using lacquer and, later, ice to stiffen garden netting hung from a few supports. After finding the resulting shells remarkably stiff for their thickness, he developed the modelling process to form the basis of a viable design procedure

for full-size structures. Using such physical models has the enormous advantage that it is not necessary to penetrate deeply into mathematics to find families of possible shapes for shells. Indeed, unlike cylindrical and hyperbolic-paraboloid shells, these hanging shapes cannot be described geometrically using a few mathematical equations, which means that an engineer could not analyse them anyway.

By establishing the form using a model, the statical design has only to ensure that the shell is thick enough to withstand local buckling and the stress concentrations which arise at the edges

of the shell and around the supports at ground level. Using models about 500 mm wide, Isler applies a uniform load to an elastic sheet and measures the deformed shape to an accuracy of about one twentieth of a millimetre. The dimensions are then scaled up fifty or a hundred times to the size of the shell to be constructed and used as the basis for setting out the formwork for the concrete. Each shell of the sports hall at Norwich spans some 48 metres to cover a usable floor area of 37 x 18.5 metres.

One of the keys to Isler's success with shells – he has constructed many hundreds since 1955 – is the standardised formwork elements he has helped to develop. These can be used repeatedly on one project, or adapted for reuse on new projects. Glulam timber beams are supported on steel trestles and thin strips of timber layed across the beams. On this layer is placed what will become the interior surface of the roof – slabs of wood-wool and sometimes sprayed polyurethane insulation. Upon this is placed the steel reinforcement – generally two layers of 6 mm steel in a 100 mm

mesh – and the insulation is then attached to this using a plastic fixing (to reduce cold bridging) and stainless-steel wire. Much more reinforcement is needed in the vicinity of the supports.

The concrete mix contains both plasticiser and retarder, allowing it to be worked by hand during the two days needed to pour and finish each shell. After a further few days the roof is given an initial prestress in the perimeter ground beams which pull the corners a little towards each other. After 21 days when the concrete has developed sufficient strength, the remaining prestress is applied by pulling the corners in a little further; this causes the entire shell to be lifted off its centering. This prestress also ensures that the shell does not deflect under its own weight or snow load in a way that would bring part of the concrete surface into tension: good water resistance with no further treatment is thus ensured.

Further reading

Concrete Quarterly, No. 173, summer 1992, pp. 24–26
Concrete Quarterly, No. 175, winter 1992, pp. 12–15
Heinz Isler: Schalen, Katalog zur Ausstellung, Karl Krämer Verlag, 1989
David Billington, The Tower and the Bridge, 1983

Aviary

Munich Zoo 1980

Structural engineer   Buro Happold

Architect   Jorg Gribl with Frei Otto

Client   Tierpark AG

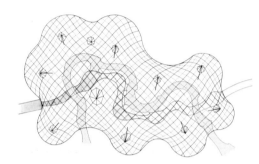

The architect's vision for an aviary to cover about 4500 square metres was 'a structure like a cloud'. The interior should be impeded by as little structure as possible and the boundary surface should allow small birds (and wind) to pass through freely, but be a barrier to large birds and predators.

Throughout the project two strands of design development progressed simultaneously, with ideas constantly passing from one to the other. A form had to be found which satisfied both architectural and structural constraints, and suitable materials, connections and construction processes had to be evolved which would enable the form to be built.

The idea of using a steel mesh as the material of the boundary surface presented itself early on, but it was not clear how such a net might withstand snow loads of up to 0.4 kN/m². The original idea of hanging a lightweight mesh beneath a grid of taut cables was abandoned because it was felt it would look rather 'baggy' in the snowy conditions that Munich often experiences. Better would be a taut net which could somehow carry these imposed loads by stretching like an elastic sheet; but a mesh of steel wires strong enough to carry the forces would be too stiff to give the desired elasticity. And then a solution was noticed, literally within sight of the proposed aviary: a mesh made of crimped steel wires as used in some of the animal cages elsewhere in the zoo.

Not only would a mesh of crimped wires have the right stress/strain characteristics for the elastic net, it would

also provide adequate safety should the mesh be overloaded beyond the steel's elastic limit, since it could deform easily in a plastic manner while retaining adequate strength. And, finally, the crimping prevents the wires sliding past one another so that the holes in the mesh do not become enlarged.

Most importantly, the crimped mesh would be able to sustain large in-plane shear deformations with little resistance. This property is essential in a tensioned cable structure since it is by this means that a net is able to find its own shape when stretched over a number of supports. Nevertheless, the angle of shear has to be limited to about 40° otherwise the net goes slack in one direction and produces unsightly folds which permanently deform a material such as steel.

Having devised a suitable 'material' for the boundary surface there were several further matters to resolve. How could the mesh be made to take up a shape which would satisfy the architect's vision of a free-form geometry while being taut enough to work as an elastic sheet and not be vibrated by the wind like the fabric of a conventional tent? How would the homogenous mesh be supported from just a few points without causing unacceptable stress concentrations? How would a continuous net of some 5000 square metres be manufactured and erected? And, not least, how would the precise form of the net be established and defined and its structural performance and safety confirmed. In other words, how would it be designed?

By suspending the mesh from a number of masts any number of suitable forms for the boundary surface could be created. Its profile could be controlled in several ways, depending on the number, position and height of the masts, the use of tie-downs at points between the masts and the precise shape of the unsheared mesh. Once a form had been created, and because the surface would be anticlastic (doubly-curved in opposing directions), the net could be tensioned by fixing it down around the perimeter and at the tie-downs, and by tightening the cables that tie the net to the mastheads. By this means of pre-stressing, sufficient tension could be introduced into the net to limit its movement when buffeted by the wind.

It was first proposed to overcome the problem of stress concentrations in the net at the mast supports by means of a mushroom head, supported in turn by cables from the mast top. This idea would have avoided a major perforation of the mesh but was abandoned because of anticipated difficulties during construction and the need to erect the aviary over a mature ash tree. An alternative system was devised using a pantograph system of cables and linked mesh-clamps. These collect the load from every mesh filament around the perimeter of a roughly circular hole in the net and concentrate them into just four adjustable cables attached to each masthead. The hole is 'patched' and a seal around the mast effected by a section of unstressed mesh.

The woven mesh of 3.2 mm crimped stainless-steel wires was available in rolls 2.5 metres wide, and sections of mesh were pre-assembled in the factory into rolls 12.5 metres wide and 40 or 50 metres long. This was only made possible by using the newly developed argon shield technology (TIG) to butt-weld the stainless steel wires – sixteen for every metre of edge. These larger sections were welded together on site before being lifted into position.

For the architect the form of the structure was only constrained by its function, the site and his vision. For the structural engineer the form was constrained also by how it might work as a structure, and how he might be able to justify this expectation. The first stage in this process was to make a number of models of the aviary to help visualise and develop its architectural form and its structural concept, form and behaviour. These models were invaluable in experimenting with the geometry of the complex curved surface and seeing how the masts and tie-downs might be best arranged.

While small models are invaluable in generating forms and can demonstrate that the overall structural concept is sound, they are of limited help to the engineer when it comes to matters of

detail. Such models are dangerously misleading in many crucial respects – model struts and ties are disproportionately strong and stiff, and a model net has elastic and shearing properties that are not at all representative of a full-size steel cable net. Such inherent difficulties in scaling up forces and deformations on a small model to a full-size tension structure mean that they cannot provide the engineer with an adequate justification of the expected behaviour of the structure. A further problem is that the geometry of this class of structure is a naturally generated form and not one which can be described by a mathematical equation, as is the case with a cylindrical or hyperbolic-paraboloid shell. In order for engineers to analyse the forces in a structure, they must be able to describe the form mathematically.

Finding the precise geometry and forces in a simple tension structure such as a chain is not at all difficult. The principal complexity in a cable net is the sheer number of mathematical equations to solve, and this was only made economically possible as the power of computers grew. For a flexible tension surface the forces and stresses in the system depend upon its geometry, and vice versa: an iterative approach is therefore called for. A surface geometry is specified, based on approximate measurements taken from the small models and hand calculations, and the forces are computed. Any out-of-balance forces tend to deform the (computer) model to a new geometry, which is then taken as the start of a new calculation

cycle, and so on, until an equilibrium state is reached. In this manner the equilibrium shape and forces in the net and supports can be found for the many different combinations of static, prestressing, wind and snow loads.

With the development of this approach to designing tension structures, another possibility arose. The geometrical model of the cable net generated by the computer could help define with great accuracy the dimensions of the flat areas of mesh that would need to be 'stitched' together along their edges, and of the many cables and masts in the structure. In this way the need for adjustable masts and cables, equivalent to the guy ropes of a conventional tent, could be avoided and an altogether more elegant appearance achieved.

Further reading

Patterns, No. 5, Buro Happold, 1989, pp. 29–32
Structural Engineering Review, July 1994

Connection

Structural connections or joints are the means of linking parts of a structural framework together in order to transfer loads. They can also be the means by which an engineer controls how a structure works as a whole; in order that a roof structure works as a truss, for instance, it is essential that one support can freely move horizontally. The joints in a structure have a powerful influence on how it looks; they can even be the primary structural characteristic of a building.

Joints can fulfil one or more distinct functions. They may be used to transmit direct loads in tension or compression where no bending is involved – the pin-joint. But conversely, a pin-joint can be introduced into a frame structure in order to ensure that no bending is transmitted. Structural members can be linked by a moment connection when the engineer wants to transfer bending through the joint – the basis of portal or Vierendeel action. Moving into three dimensions, a joint may be required to carry torsion; for instance, to provide restraint against lateral torsional buckling. Each of these types of load transfer also involves transmitting shear forces which must always be an additional, if secondary design consideration.

When certain movements must be prevented, or allowed, it is necessary to consider the number of degrees of freedom in a connection – up to six linear and six rotational. By this means, thermal movements of the main structure can be isolated from the more delicate structure in a building façade. A joint may also need to incorporate a device such as a spring, which will allow the load that it transmits to depend on its movement, or *vice versa*.

Joints can be classified as either articulated or monolithic. Some materials can be used to make joints of either type, while others are best suited to only one category. In-situ concrete, for example, is ideally suited for making monolithic joints that will automatically transmit bending. Steel, on the other hand, can be made into a monolithic joint by welding or bolting, or into an articulated connection using a single pin, ball-and-socket, or as a tube within a tube to create a sliding joint.

The form of a joint depends on many factors – the job it has to perform, the material or materials to be connected and the shapes and relative disposition of the adjoining members. It is also necessary to make sensible and economical use of the material in fabrication and construction and to ensure easy assembly of discrete elements. Finally there is the designer's own intellectual approach, which can range from mechanistic to sculptural to anthropomorphic.

Joints are the key to harmonious structures. The challenge for the designer is to produce joints which clearly communicate their function – the job they are actually doing – and to do this in an efficient and elegant way. There is immense satisfaction in discovering the appropriate solution, for it is easy to design an ugly joint, much more difficult to design an elegant one.

Tony Hunt

Sackler Galleries

Royal Academy of Arts

London 1991

Structural engineer   Albert Williamson-Taylor

YRM-Anthony Hunt Associates

Architect   Foster Associates

Client   Royal Academy of Arts

Inserting a new structure into an old building is always challenging, especially when the building is Grade I listed and devoted to the display of fine art. The architect's scheme for refurbishing the Royal Academy included using the otherwise dead space between the two original buildings to provide stair and lift access to the upper gallery floors. The engineer's challenge was to achieve this in an elegant way while imposing only the very minimum of new loads onto the structure of the existing buildings.

The steel and glass staircase and the landing floors at two upper levels are all supported by, and cantilevered out from,

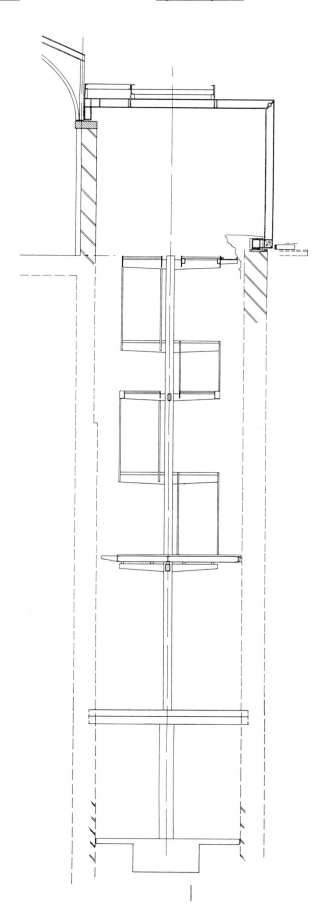

just two circular columns, 245 mm in diameter. This slender free-standing structure is given lateral restraint at the upper level where the columns are supported by the horizontal Vierendeel of the glass bridge structure. The bridge is tied in turn to the new, concrete floor plates which carry any lateral loads by shear action back to the end walls and thence to the ground.

Nevertheless, the 9-metre-high structure is too slender to gain the necessary lateral stability only by restraining the ends. The additional stiffness is provided by the stairs themselves. The glass treads are supported in 30 mm x 20 mm stainless-steel angles which are welded to form a rectangle. These are bolted to the stringers and together these form a filigree Vierendeel girder rising the full height of the structure.

A roof had to be provided over this new space between the two buildings. It could only be made light enough to be

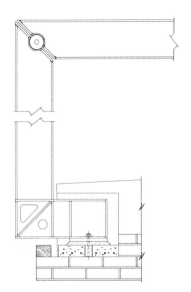

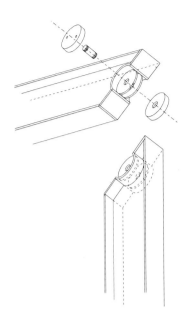

supported by the existing walls as long as the new structure exerted no <u>horizontal</u> forces on the walls. This requirement was achieved in two ways.

At roof level, steel beams are joined to the columns by pin-joints to ensure that no bending is transmitted through the joint and that the columns carry only vertical loads. The foot of each column is 'cranked' to ensure that the vertical load in the column is applied precisely along the centre-line of the old masonry wall. To ensure the pin-joint can be rotated by even a minute bending moment, the diameter of the pin is made small. Frictional resistance is thus minimal and any rust which might form would be easily fractured. However, such a small pin would have appeared out of scale and an ingenious detail was needed to overcome this problem.

Further reading

<u>Architectural Review</u>, December 1991, pp. 56–61

Aviary

Hong Kong Park

Hong Kong 1991

Structural engineers   Brian Forster, Alistair Day, John White

Ove Arup & Partners

Architect   Wong Tung & Partners

Client   Royal Hong Kong Jockey Club

In most buildings – from compression structures such as masonry cathedrals to modern braced frames – it is the notional (invisible) line of thrust which moves in response to imposed loads to suit a certain equilibrium state. Actual movements of the structure, needed to develop the forces that resist imposed loads, are relatively small.

Among the types of structure normally used in buildings, tension structures are unique in that in order to establish their state of statical equilibrium, they find their own shape and in doing so may need to move by a relatively large amount. Anyone who has hung washing on a clothes line will have observed this.

Tension structures such as cable nets and fabric tent structures are also characterised by being prestressed; the net or fabric needs to be held taut by forces locked into the structure to give the surfaces some resistance to flapping in wind.

There are two important consequences of these properties of tension structures. The first is that the geometry of such a structure will change significantly during construction as it is hung in position and gradually tensioned to the required level of prestress. The second is that it is essential to be able to predict the _final_ geometry of the structure before it is built in order that cables, nets, panels or fabrics can be cut to precise sizes without the need for thousands of adjustable connectors or guy ropes in an otherwise lightweight, even diaphanous, structure.

It is for these reasons that the computer has been so invaluable to the designers of modern tension structures such as sports stadia and aviaries. Previously, physical models had to be used, but it is no easy matter to make small models which faithfully reproduce the material and structural characteristics of full-size components. It is even more difficult to scale up measurements made on 1:50 or 1:100 models to make full-size components to an accuracy of a few millimetres.

The principle of the Hong Kong Park Aviary is simple: a light, bird-proof mesh hung from a cable net pulled down over three tubular steel arches. The detail was more complex. It was a delicate matter to balance the relative stiffnesses of arch and cable net. The arch supports

the cable net and the cable net stabilises the arch to prevent buckling; however, the thinner the arch, the stiffer the net must be to provide the restraint necessary to inhibit buckling. On the other hand, the thicker the arch, the stiffer it is and the greater the load it attracts and, hence, the sturdier it needs to be.

The site chosen for the aviary presented additional problems – it is in a wooded, steep-sided and meandering valley. Establishing the ground geometry was a difficult enough task, in addition there was the problem of how to represent the geometry of the boundary wall of the cable net as a mathematical

model in a structural analysis computer program. This extremely complex geometrical problem was solved by feeding the data from the site survey into a program more normally used for planning the route of roads through undulating landscapes. It is no exaggeration to say that this would have been impossible to achieve to the required degree of accuracy in the time available using manual calculations. Although computers have gained the reputation of being able to solve many and complex equations in structural and stress analysis, it is easy to overlook the benefit they have contributed by being able to perform (merely!) intricate geometrical calculations.

With the geometry of the cable-net boundary in the computer, the final geometry of the surface was established by performing the computer equivalent of pulling, little by little, an elastic net over the steel arches down to the boundary wall.

From this model could be calculated with precision the lengths of the cables and the angles at which they would have to be joined to one another, the arches

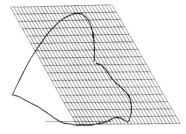

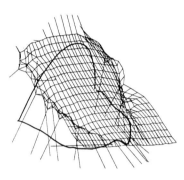

or the boundary wall. But a mathematical model is one thing, a real cable net something else. It would have been both expensive and unwise to have made all the cables and connectors with no possibility of adjustment; and in any case most of the connectors needed to be capable of movement during the assembly and prestressing operations.

It was a particular challenge in this part of the design to devise appropriate connectors. Between the cables of the cable net a clamp can be tightened to grip the pairs of cables crossing at any angle between 90° and 0°. The mesh is suspended from the cable net by V-shaped stirrups, which are free to move like the links of a chain. The anchorages of the cables to the boundary wall have to carry particularly large forces, yet the precise angles of the cables, and hence the forces, could not be predicted by the computer to a sufficiently high degree of precision. A single, strong, adaptable

connector was thus needed to cope with almost any three-dimensional angle between cable and anchorage.

The solution was a two-part base plate – a moveable upper part clamped to a circular base which is bolted to the boundary wall. The upper part could be rotated freely about the vertical axis to suit any position around the boundary wall and could be given minor adjustments during erection of the cable net and after partial tensioning of the cable net and mesh. Only then was the moveable upper part welded to the fixed lower part. Subsequent minor rotations about any axis can be accommodated in the spherical bearing which joins the cable termination to the base plate.

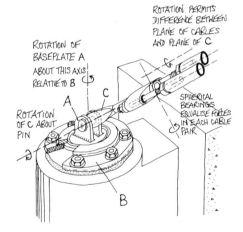

Further reading

Arup Journal, Vol. 26 No. 2, summer 1991, pp. 11–13
L'Arca, No. 57, February 1992, pp. 82–85

Tree House

Stoke Pero, Somerset 1979

Structural engineer   **Price & Myers**

Architect   **Beaver Associates**

Client   **Chris Beaver**

The architect wanted to build a tree house for his children, but the only trees available were pines which do not have suitable branches. His first proposal was that the house should span between two trees, on a single beam supported by steel hoops around each trunk and stabilised by struts. The loading would be wind and three children jumping. A dialogue developed.

The engineer suggested using parallel twin beams either side of the tree trunks. A single bolt through the beams and the trunk would form a joint which would both support the house and resist overturning loads due to the wind. The entire house would then be supported at only two points and stabilising struts could be avoided. Also, by bolting the beams together through the trunks, the hoops would not be needed and chafing damage to the bark could be virtually eliminated.

Then there was the question of relative movement between the two trees during a gale. To restrain such movements large loads would have to be carried through the tree house and this would need additional structural material; but these loads could be avoided almost entirely by allowing some relative movement between the trees rather than trying to prevent it. This was achieved simply by elongating the bolt-hole through the beams at one of the tree house's two supports to allow up to 150 mm of longitudinal movement; the bolt bears on PTFE-bearing strips in the slots.

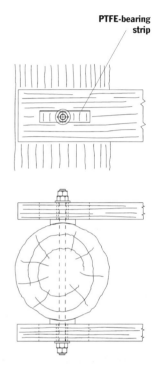

PTFE-bearing strip

Waterloo International Terminal

London 1993

Structural engineer	Alan Jones, Mike Otlet
	YRM-Anthony Hunt Associates
Cladding contractor	Briggs Amasco Curtain Wall Limited
Architect	Nicholas Grimshaw & Partners
Client	British Railways Board

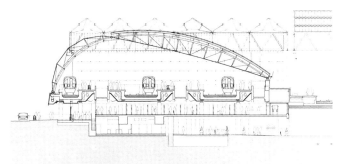

Both the form and the construction of this station roof were strongly influenced by the site. There had to be adequate headroom over a track near the site boundary and the roof would have to follow the complex geometry of the platforms along their 400-metre length. It would also need to provide support for cladding and glazing, and suffer no sudden changes of appearance along its length.

The solution was developed by the structural engineers, architects and cladding contractors collaborating closely. A skeletal frame had to be developed which would accommodate the changing span and articulation in plan: the glazing and cladding systems would have to bridge between the ribs, whatever their spacing and orientation, without losing the construction benefits of standardisation. The key to this solution lay in the development of a range of connections between the cladding and frame which would carry the necessary loads and allow a large variety of relative movements between the glazing, frame and platform structure.

The roof is a triangulated structure – two curved trusses are joined at the apex and tied at their lower ends through the platform structure. The pin-jointed connections allow the ends of the trusses to rotate as they move in response to differential support movement and wind, snow and thermal loads, and ensure that no turning moments are transmitted to the platform structure. They also served to reduce the number of connections that had to be made at the final erection stage of each pair of trusses.

Each of the trusses has a section and elevation corresponding to the bending moments it must withstand, both vertically and longitudinally. They are also conceived as structural reflections of one another. The outer compression chord of the larger span is formed from twin tubes, while the tension chord and the correspondingly delicate members and connections are on the inside of the building. The smaller span supporting the glazing has its filigree trussing rods on the outside of the curved compression member. Together they form a more transparent structure than if the smaller truss had been identical in form to the larger one. The tubular struts between the chords of the trusses taper throughout their length to correspond to the size of elements at either end. Cast-steel

nodes within the tension chords simplify the connection of the incoming rods at several different angles.

The result is a roof which appears to be a smooth and gradually diminishing arch along the length of the platforms. Yet the roof is not a true arch from the structural point of view: by conceiving it as a pair of pinned trusses which act in bending, but whose members themselves sustain virtually no bending, a visually much lighter-weight structure was achieved. In addition, its clarity is enhanced by means of the various connectors which allow the cladding and glazing to float clear of the ribs.

With two and a half acres of glazing to fit it was essential that as much regularity as possible be achieved in the sizes of the glass panels. This was espe-

cially difficult given that the surface curves in three dimensions between supports whose separation varies considerably. In the fully-glazed west wall, each of the 36 bays is unique and fully adjustable connections were necessary. It was also realised that there would be great advantage if all the glazing panels could be the same size and hung from a single type of floating, extruded-aluminium glazing bar.

Ultimately glass is not very forgiving – even a small twist in a flat plate can lead to fracture. Before the connection could be designed many different variables had to be investigated, beginning with the magnitude and direction of the many possible loads on the connections.

Some of the loads would be induced directly – the self-weight of the glass and its supporting framework, snow load, wind blowing on the glass or sucking the glazing off the roof, loads transmitted from adjacent glazing panels, impact by a maintenance worker or falling (dead!) swan.

Other loads on the glass can arise from the relative movements of the various supports – deflection and expansion of the glazing bars, and movement of the purlins and the trusses to which they are fixed. The latter could, in turn, arise from many causes – snow and wind loads on the roof; the effects of temperature on the ribs and the longitudinal bracing; movement of the entire platform structure on which the roof is built, caused by the weight of trains; and longitudinal forces induced by trains coming to a sudden halt. In addition there is

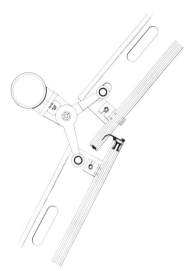
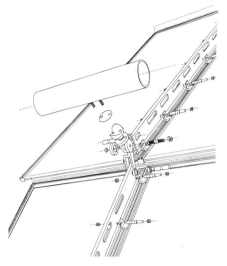
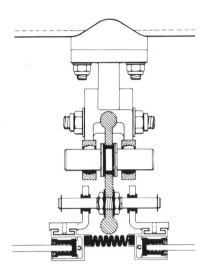

the movement of the concrete platform structure as it contracts during its curing process (for up to five years after construction) and very long-term movements of the ground on which the entire new station is built, a result of removing the previous heavy masonry platform structure.

All these loads had to be calculated and converted into movements of the various parts of the entire system. Thus the full range of possible relative positions between truss and glazing could be established as well as the most suitable directions in which it would be prudent to allow the glazing to move relative to the trusses in order to prevent movement-induced loads.

A further requirement was to clad the conical shape of the roof with indentical, rectangular glass panels in each bay and achieve a fully-sealed envelope. This was realised by means of concertina seals between each panel in the longitudinal direction and a wiper blade in the circumferential direction.

A single type of fixing was devised, made of cast stainless steel. It has two

radial arms which can be locked at any angle relative to the horizontal tubular purlins and to each other. Different junctions between the components have different degrees of freedom to move, either by sliding or rotating. One of the radial arms is fixed rigidly to a glazing bar in two axes and free to slide and rotate in the other. The other arm is fixed relative to a glazing bar in only one axis and is free to slide in two other axes, but rotate in only one of these. The fixing between the glass itself and the glazing bar is restrained in two axes and free to slide in the third, but still able to rotate in all three directions. The result is that the entire glazed wall can move longitudinally relative to the supporting structure.

The final solution looks very simple, but this disguises many, many hours of thought along the way. As for the steel cladding and the two glazed walls – one hanging between the original station roof and the new platforms, the other between the platform structure and the floor at road level – that's another story, or, rather, three!

Further reading

Architectural Review, September 1993, pp. 26–44
The Structural Engineer, Vol. 72 No. 8, 19 April 1994, pp. 123–130
New Civil Engineer, 27 May 1993, pp. 18–23

Ponds Forge
International Sports Centre

Sheffield 1991

Structural engineer for roof
John Gregory, Neil Carstairs
Ove Arup & Partners

Architect **FaulknerBrowns**
Client **Sheffield City Council**

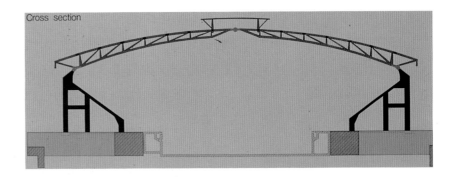
Cross section

The idea for the roof over the pool at Ponds Forge had its origins in the ribs of a Gothic, vaulted masonry roof. In the modern context, the ribs are curved steel girders forming a three-pin arch, though this is not an arch in the structural sense since the girders must withstand substantial bending as well as pure compression. The girders (which, on structural grounds, could have been straight) are pinned at each end of the span and where they meet in the centre. By making the joints in the form of hinges, turning moments in one axis are virtually eliminated. A further advantage of the three-pin arch is that changes of temperature, rather than leading to large stresses within the structure and the need for heavier members, can be accommodated by the movement of the roof. Pin-joints are one of many means by which a structural engineer can make a structure behave in a prescribed and, hence, better under-

stood way; they also make the structural analysis easier.

The roof spans nearly 55 metres and is extremely flat. This was achieved largely by incorporating all the ventilation equipment and ducts beneath and behind the seating rather than hanging from the roof – the headroom could thus be lower and the structure lighter since it needs to carry a smaller imposed load. However, the large span-to-rise ratio (8.7) leads to very large lateral thrusts on the side supports.

The eaves joint had to be designed to transmit a total of some 330 tonnes from the two roof trusses, which meet at 55° on plan, to the concrete abutment. It was necessary to incorporate a pin-joint in one axis and a spherical bearing to permit lateral twisting when the roof is loaded asymmetrically. The joint also had to carry the tubular struts which support the upper member of the trusses where they project outwards beyond the hinge.

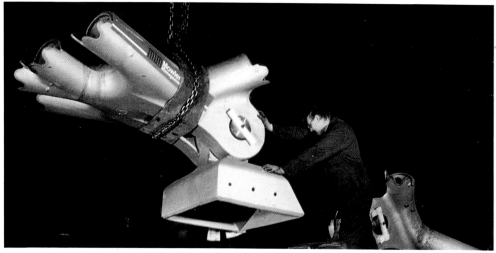

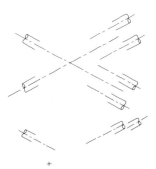 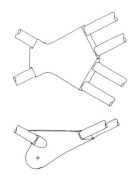 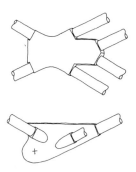 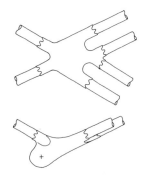

A casting was preferred from the outset for this important joint as it would allow the freedom to sculpt a functional and visually striking component. The design evolved through many versions, from the raw geometric requirements to an arrangement which was well-suited to the casting process, provided the most streamlined load path through the casting, avoided awkward welds between tubes and the casting, and which would use as little metal as possible. The result was a connection that was cheaper than the fabricated alternative.

Although the casting is solid, apart from the obvious holes, it is designed to carry the loads in its outer shell so that the small flaws inevitable in castings could be more easily detected and repaired. Loads from the tubes are transferred to the casting through a circumferential weld, whose detail is perhaps not immediately apparent.

After fabrication the outer end of each roof truss was left with three bare tubes, the bottom pair of which would be received by the eaves casting when lowered in situ. As it would clearly be difficult to manoeuvre the heavy and unwieldy truss and slot the tubes into circular sockets, the casting was made with the top half of each socket absent. It was thus possible to locate the truss tubes precisely by simply lowering them into the waiting socket cups and welding the tubes and the top half of the cups in position. However, if the sockets had had straight ends, the weld joining the casting to the tube would not have been long enough to carry the forces from tube to casting. By forming a scalloped end, the length of the weld was increased by about 50 per cent.

At the other end of the casting, unsightly holding-down bolts were avoided by designing the connection as a compression joint and cementing the hollow shell of the casting onto the concrete frame, rather in the manner of a crown glued onto the stub of a tooth.

Further reading

<u>The Architects' Journal</u>, 17 July 1991, pp. 43–45
<u>Arup Journal</u>, Vol. 26 No. 2, 1991, pp. 3–9

Material

In every aspect of the way in which a material is used in a structure, the very essence of that material is on show – an essence that goes far deeper than mere material properties such as strength and stiffness. Deepest of all is how the material gets used – both alone and in combination with other materials – the means by which it is shaped, joined and manufactured into useful artefacts. Together all this constitutes a material's engineering *aesthetic*, its very soul.

With cast iron, for instance – and it matters whether it is brittle, Victorian, cast iron or the modern, malleable material – its soul is there in the surface texture and shapes made possible by the casting process, the appropriate structural forms (according to whether it is being used in tension, compression or bending, in conjunction with wrought-iron ties, brick jack-arches or a wrought-iron beam), the means by which it can be connected to other elements, and so on.

Likewise, the soul of timber is there in the dimensions of structural components and the shape of nails and screws driven into it; the soul of glass is there in the details of fixings which must avoid any undue stress concentration; the soul of wrought iron is there in the shape of rolled sections and the appearance of a hand-closed rivet; the soul of aluminium is there in the extruded shape of a glazing bar and even in the gaps needed to prevent cold bridging; the soul of concrete is there in the surface pattern of the formwork and the hue of a polished granite aggregate; the soul of mild steel is there in a cast connector, welded to a rolled-beam section, and even in its smell – try getting close to a freshly drilled or sawn girder if you doubt this.

When using a material a designer can choose whether or not to put it on show – to be seen, appreciated, and marvelled at. It is in the skill of the designer to reveal, show off, and to celebrate its aesthetic. A good engineer will use a material in harmony with its essential qualities; a poor one will awkwardly try to use one material as if it were another. Architects should be aware that they can cause engineers great distress if they insist on using a material in a way that conflicts with its essential characteristics.

The basis of engineering is knowledge of the materials being used: knowledge of what they are made of, how they are made, how they are shaped, how you fit them together, how they stand up to stress, how they break, how they catch fire, how they react to all the various agencies of ruin which are perpetually nibbling at them, how in due course all fall down.

Alan Harris

A design ... can be tactile when a material is used to express its inner nature with feeling and is clearly the work of a designer who, in thinking about the material, has made the perception of the material more real. ... The search for the authentic character of a material is at the heart of any approach to engineering design.

Peter Rice

Chapel

Fitzwilliam College, Cambridge 1991

Structural engineer   Robert Pugh

                 Ove Arup & Partners

Architect   MacCormac . Jamieson . Prichard

Client   Fitzwilliam College, Cambridge

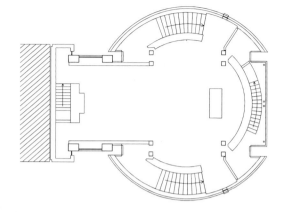

A new building in a context rich in architectural heritage assumes a great responsibility to the tradition of quality. The architecture of this chapel refers back to a classical heritage while employing modern techniques of construction to traditional materials. The structural engineer was able to help to realise these goals by virtue of a familiarity with the properties and manufacturing processes of many different materials. He was thus able to combine them successfully within the total building design and provide the detailing for practical construction.

The building concept comprises an

outer protective skin around an inner core. However, the building is not simply a shell around a core – the elements are connected both visually and physically and are integral to the whole. Thus the manner and details of their structural performance, interconnection and assembly become very important. Each of the building elements was required to perform different functions and to respond to different aesthetic, environmental or structural demands. The different building materials were selected for their particular properties, which were most appropriate to the dominant demand imposed on each element.

As a result of earlier experience on a residential building at Fitzwilliam, and on other projects where visual elements had been used to serve structural functions, the architect and engineer had already developed a vocabulary of finely-detailed precast-concrete elements, and these were further refined for the internal frame of the chapel.

The two exterior walls are of in-situ concrete and clad in brick. Being curved in plan, each behaves structurally as a thin shell and acts as a cantilever fixed at the foundations and with a deep structural section (i.e. high second moment of area); together they give the building all the lateral stability it needs. An internal frame of four precast-concrete columns and beams supports a central in-situ-concrete flat roof. A second series of four columns supports two beams which provide a springing for eleven pairs of delicate V-shaped oak struts. These in turn support a timber

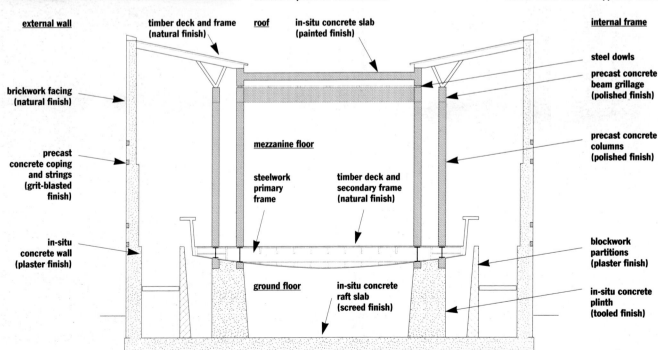

external wall

timber deck and frame
(natural finish)

roof   in-situ concrete slab
(painted finish)

internal frame

brickwork facing
(natural finish)

precast
concrete coping
and strings
(grit-blasted
finish)

in-situ
concrete wall
(plaster finish)

mezzanine floor

steelwork
primary
frame

timber deck and
secondary frame
(natural finish)

ground floor   in-situ concrete
raft slab
(screed finish)

steel dowls

precast concrete
beam grillage
(polished finish)

precast concrete
columns
(polished finish)

blockwork
partitions
(plaster finish)

in-situ concrete
plinth
(tooled finish)

side roof between the outer walls and central flat roof.

By polishing the concrete a marble-like quality was given to the delicate elements; for the more robust elements, sand blasting or tooling was used to give the concrete the appearance of stone building blocks. A variety of connections between the different materials in the floor, wall and roof elements was developed according to how strongly they were to be expressed.

The building thus represents not just a stage in the development of an architect's own work but the collaboration of architect and engineer in developing and refining the use of materials within a particular building system.

Further reading

The Architects' Journal, 1 July 1992, pp. 24–37
Architectural Review, April 1992, pp. 26–33

The Glass House

1992

Structural engineer **Dewhurst Macfarlane and Partners**   Architect   **Rick Mather Architects**

At first glance – with the Palm House at Kew in mind, or Glasgow's Kibble Palace or modern structural glazing in façades such as Peter Rice's wall at La Villette – the idea of removing entirely what little metal these structures utilise may not seem an especially significant step to take. They all have a structural system of iron or steel which can carry loads should one or more glass sheets fail. However, to make a structure, no matter how small, entirely of glass demands a totally different approach when calculating the strength of the structure and addressing the safety issues associated with the possibility of failure.

The structural capabilities of glass have long been overlooked, partly, perhaps, because its reputation is coloured by the ease with which a window or wine glass can be broken. Yet a window made of standard 4 mm glass can withstand the force of a hurricane. It is not that glass lacks strength; rather, that its strength can be very variable. It is also prone to sudden and brittle fracture – for this reason suppliers are reluctant to publish strengths for glass. It is now

some 60 years since it was recognised that glass can have a tensile strength approaching that of steel, but it is a strength which is largely lost when the surface of the glass sustains the slightest damage. Even the touch of a soft feather creates microscopic cracks which can propagate with ease and cause a brittle fracture when only a modest stress is applied.

Once recognised, this type of failure could be avoided by encasing freshly drawn glass fibres in a relatively soft resin to form the material now known as fibreglass. The resin serves both to protect the fibres from damage and to prevent them slipping past one another by carrying the shear forces associated with, for instance, bending. The use of a great many fibres has two further structural benefits – the idea of 'safety in numbers' makes it statistically unlikely that more than a few fibres will be weakened by surface damage; and should a crack in the glass start to run, it will be limited to one fibre and not cross the soft resin to adjacent fibres.

Nowadays there are two types of glass that can be used in heavily-loaded glazing – toughened and laminated glass. The former is made by cooling float glass very suddenly during manufacture so that, when finished, the surface is held in compression by the glass inside, which is stressed in tension. Cracks in the surface are thus not subject to tension under moderate bending loads and cannot spread to cause brittle fracture. However, should a crack penetrate the compressed skin, it will propagate freely

through the central tension zone and the glass will shatter in an explosive manner. Laminated glass is made of several layers of float or toughened glass bonded together with a polyester resin. Its effectiveness is based on the same principles as fibreglass.

These ideas were all brought together when considering how glass could be used as a 'normal' load-bearing material in a situation where a real possibility of overloading, a manufacturing flaw or accidental damage, could cause any sheet of glass to crack. Laminated float glass could not be used because it is prone to cracking around holes; neither could a beam of toughened glass because of the catastrophic consequences of a single crack. As is often the case, the solution, with hindsight, was obvious.

Two sheets of toughened glass, each capable of carrying the loads, could be bonded together to form a beam; should one crack, the other could take the load – at least until a new beam could be fitted. But how to join both sheets of the beam to a column? Even if the column were also made of two sheets, the beam would not positively locate with the column and could be easily dislodged. The solution was to increase the number of

sheets to three and the connection could then be made in the manner of a mortice and tenon timber joint. As the glass columns cantilever from ground level, the column-beam junction needs to carry only small loads and, such is the area of overlap, these can be carried by clear silicon rubber. The beams themselves are fish-bellied as a reflection of the larger bending moments towards the centre of the span.

The double glazing for the walls and roof provides the stability for the building by shear-wall action and had to be designed with the different characteristics of toughened and laminated glass – and how they fail – in mind. The final choice was toughened glass for the outer sheet and laminated for the inner. Should the outer sheet shatter on impact with a sharp object, the inner sheet would carry the loads and protect the room's occupants; should a layer of the inner laminate fail, it would be held in

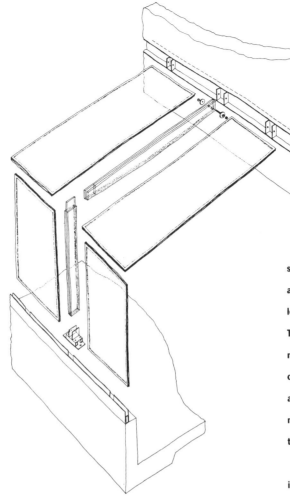

situ by the polymer laminate bonding and the outer sheet would carry the loads until a repair could be effected. The aluminium glazing beads and black mastic normally used in double glazing clearly had to be avoided to achieve an all-glass structure; an air-tight seal was made by bonding the two sheets together with a bead of glass.

The means of avoiding condensation in the sealed glazing unit turned out to yield an unexpected bonus. A Finnish firm was found which could coat glass with a thin layer of metal through which a current can be passed. This acts as a heating element inside the double glazing and prevents condensation. So effective was this technology that it was also able to provide most of the heating for the entire all-glass extension.

Further reading

<u>The Architects' Journal</u>, 22 July 1992, pp. 40–43
<u>AJ Focus</u>, July 1992, pp. 119–211
<u>Architectural Review</u>, February 1993, pp. 67–70

West Totton First School

Structural engineer <u>Buro Happold</u>

Architect <u>Hampshire County Council Architects</u>

Client <u>Hampshire County Council</u>

Hampshire 1990

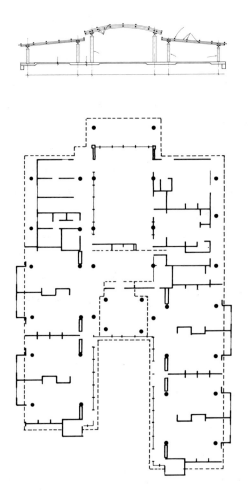

The location of this school – at the end of a short avenue of trees – inspired the choice of exposed-timber columns to support the roof and led on to the idea of making the entire structure of wood. However, timber in sufficiently large structural sections is no longer an economic option and glue-laminated timber was used as a substitute. This man-made material retains the benefits and attractions of natural timber – ease of cutting and connecting with nails, screws, glue or bolts; long life in dry conditions; warm to the touch and, not least, its appearance – while offering the added advantage of being able to

be formed into many unnatural shapes and sizes.

Making large buildings from timber to meet a wide range of modern building requirements demands an approach to design very different from that of the traditional carpenter or builder of log cabins. The Glulam components, for instance, are factory-made and pre-drilled for easy assembly on site before being lifting into position by crane. There are also differences in how the material is used structurally. All-timber structures usually have substantial opaque walls which give a building its stability by acting as shear walls. For a

school this approach would have compromised the need to introduce as much natural light as possible into the class-rooms and activity hall.

By conceiving the structure as a moment-resisting frame the external envelope would not need to carry any vertical or shear loads and could, if required, be fully glazed. Conventional steel or concrete portal frames, however, usually derive their stability from large rigid joints between columns and rafters at eaves level. In timber, this solution would have been heavy on the eye, and the alternative of fixing the columns rigidly to the foundations was explored. But such an idea is easier to imagine than to execute. A domestic solution, such as seating a post in a hole, may work for a garden fence but would not be satisfactory in a substantial building with a life of many decades. Stresses in a rigid timber connection can be very high and cause local crushing which would quickly lead to the joint becoming loose; also, both rot and corrosion in such a critical detail must be avoided at all costs.

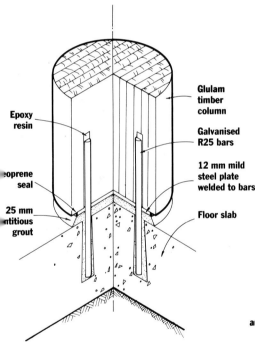

Epoxy resin

eoprene seal

25 mm ntitious grout

Glulam timber column

Galvanised R25 bars

12 mm mild steel plate welded to bars

Floor slab

These various limitations were overcome in the rigid joints at the column bases by using an epoxy resin to glue the timber to corrosion-protected steel rods. These in turn are grouted into the concrete foundations. In this way stress concentrations are avoided by maximising the area over which stresses are transferred between the two materials, and by introducing a tough resin with a modulus lower than both timber and steel to 'attract' the larger proportion

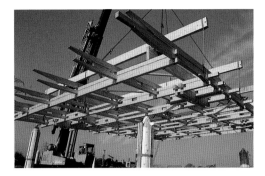

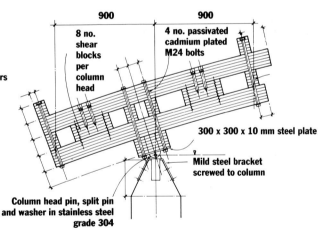

900 · 900

8 no. shear blocks per column head

4 no. passivated cadmium plated M24 bolts

300 x 300 x 10 mm steel plate

Mild steel bracket screwed to column

Column head pin, split pin and washer in stainless steel grade 304

of any deformations.

At the top of each column the problem is inverted: the pin-joint serves to ensure that no bending moments can be transferred from the relatively stiff column to the slender roof members which would otherwise need to be more substantial. The joint detail itself also ensures that loads from the roof are transferred effectively to the full section of the timber without giving rise to high local stresses.

While obviously exploiting to the full the properties of the material, the designers have also conceived the structure of the building to express the very properties that give timber its own unique aesthetic. This structure would look like timber even if it were painted or otherwise disguised. By the shapes, sizes and relative disposition of the elements, the form and manner of the joints between elements and the connections with components of other materials, it is possible to see and understand that the material is timber without having to rely on visual clues from the colour and grain.

Further reading

AJ Focus, June 1991, pp. 15–19
Patterns, No. 8, Buro Happold, pp. 2–9

Trinity College Book Store

Cambridge 1991

Structural engineer Peter Leveridge

Harris & Sutherland

Client Trinity College, Cambridge

Soil is probably the most challenging material that structural engineers have to deal with. It is not made in factories and its properties can never be known as reliably as those of steel, timber or even concrete. Furthermore, its engineering properties depend utterly on the presence (or absence) of water and whether the soil particles have been disturbed from their natural state – for instance, by excavation.

The urgent need for additional book storage space at Trinity College presented various problems as there were few acceptable possibilities for introducing new buildings into the medieval court. A scheme was proposed for a new store beneath a narrow, enclosed wedge of land by the River Cam, adjacent to Wren's library. This led to a number of engineering challenges: gaining access to the site, ensuring long-term watertightness against a 5-metre head of water, minimising any disturbance to the water-logged soil around the site and, of course, leaving the adjacent structures undamaged. To maximise the space for books, the basement walls had to be placed as close as possible to existing buildings – 300 mm from a Victorian building and 2 metres from a medieval boundary wall of uncertain stability. In order that site traffic did not have to use an 18th-century masonry bridge, access to the site was provided by a Bailey bridge over the River Cam.

Construction of any basement entails the removal of a substantial weight of soil and this leads to a relief of stress on the underlying soil. When relieved of

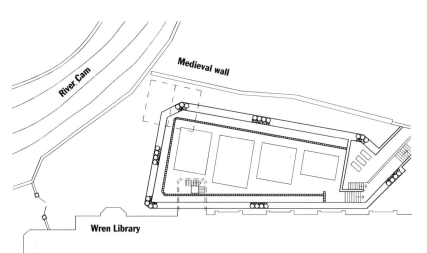

stress, the clay on this site expands as water enters the pores in the clay. Since this can exert substantial forces on any basement floor it is customary to provide a void beneath a basement into which the heaving clay can expand. This can, however, bring new problems – soil outside the excavation can migrate around the toe of the wall and might, in turn, cause subsidence of adjacent buildings.

To avoid these problems the design engineers decided to construct the building in such a way that the stress condition under the site would be disturbed as little as possible. Thus, not only would the building be literally invis-

ible, being underground, but also even the soil beneath it would hardly be affected by its construction. This was achieved by several means.

The book store takes the form of a box within a box to provide two barriers against water ingress. The outer barrier is of reinforced concrete. Inside, a suspended floor, an inner metal-clad roof and wall panelling will protect the books should any water penetrate the concrete. If necessary the panels can also give access to allow repair of the concrete walls.

The 12-metre secant piles forming the impervious structural retaining wall were formed using a continuous flight auger. In this process the concrete forming the pile is pumped down the centre of the auger, which is gradually forced out of the ground. There is thus never an empty hole which would allow the water and soil to move and hence disturb the equilibrium of the soil. The inward deflection of these piles was monitored continuously during construction so the engineer could be sure that the pressure of soil and water on the wall was not leading to unacceptable soil disturbance around the building.

The ground anchors were installed from ground level after excavation and casting of the basement floor slab. These anchors were stressed in tension to re-compress the underlying clay to its original state of stress. This solution also provided anchorage for the entire book store against the substantial buoyancy forces caused by the high groundwater level. In this manner, expansion of clay at the base of the excavation was limited to just 5 mm, and even this was partially reversed when the anchor piles were fully stressed.

Further reading

New Civil Engineer, 21 February 1991, pp. 33–35

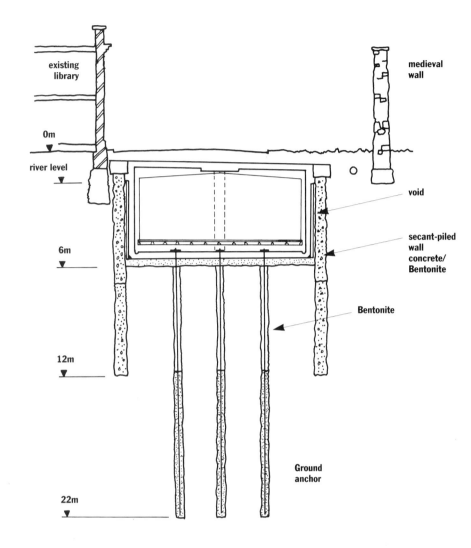

Pabellon del futuro

Expo '92

Seville 1992

Structural engineer   Peter Rice, Alistair Lenczner

Ove Arup & Partners

Architect   **MBM (Martorell, Bohigas, Mackay)**

in association with Jaime Freixa

Client   **Expo '92 SA**

Stresses in masonry structures, even spectacular ones such as Gothic cathedrals, seldom rise to more than one twentieth of the strength of the stone. Also, the most efficient shape for a freestanding masonry arch is not circular but parabolic (roughly). How, then, to devise a structure that would fully exploit the inherent strength of granite and not rely on sheer weight for its lateral stability, as would befit a 20th-century work of engineering while also referring back to the semi-circular arches of the aqueducts of Roman Spain?

The architects wanted to create a spectacular eastern façade structure to support the roof of the Pavilion of the Future, that would capture the imagination of visitors. Building the façade using natural stone as the primary structural material was seen as an opportunity to challenge contemporary perceptions of stone as purely a cladding or facing material. The result shows how modern analytical, fabrication and construction methods can enable the properties of this ancient building material to be exploited in ways appropriate to our own time.

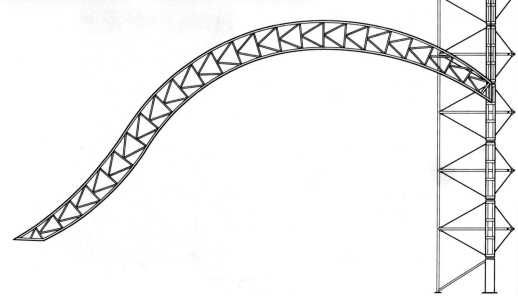

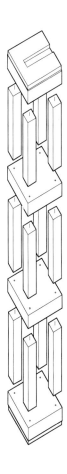

The façade of the pavilion supports the curved roof girders. By means of a series of tie-rods, these loads are applied radially to the stone arch. This distributes the load equally around the arch, which can therefore be semi-circular rather than parabolic.

The columns are 28 metres tall with an overall cross-section of just 0.64 square metres, of which just a quarter is solid stone. This degree of slenderness would be dangerously unstable if unrestrained and each column is stabilised at 5-metre intervals by means of a delicate three-dimensional steel lattice of rods and struts, rather in the manner that tendons and muscles lend stability to the inherently unstable human spine.

The columns and arches are made of prefabricated voussoirs which are them-

selves made from solid blocks of Rosa Poriño granite. These open stone voussoirs were assembled at the stoneworks using an epoxy resin glue (which is stronger than the granite) and short stainless-steel dowels to give positive location and a shear connection across the glued joint: there is no internal reinforcing of the granite pieces. The granite had to be cut with very great precision and this, indeed the entire project, was only made viable by the use of modern computer-controlled machine tools.

The prefabricated voussoirs forming the arches are joined with a cementi-

tious grout and stainless-steel dowels which locate the units and serve as shear connectors. These joints have no significant resistance to tension: in conditions of extreme load they allow hinges to form rather than high tensile stresses to develop in the granite due to bending. Computer software developed specially for non-linear structural analysis was a key element in being able to justify the stability of the stone arch. The joints between the stone voussoirs of the arch were modelled to represent the rocking mechanism associated with the formation of hinges in either the intrados or extrados, depending on the position of the line of thrust.

In the manner of traditional masonry structures, the stability of the arches

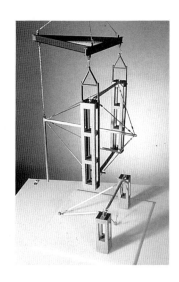

thus depends entirely on their inherent geometric stability. It is further increased by virtue of the precompression that arises from the deadweight of the pavilion roof, and is transferred to the façade via the steel tension ring.

The columns are similar except that significant shear and tension stresses in the stonework are avoided in a different way. Vertical loads are transmitted through neoprene and steel laminated bearing pads which are able to sustain some movement and therefore transmit no shear. The shear forces are transferred between adjacent prefabricated units externally through the steel stabilising structure.

The means of building the façade structure was an important consideration during its design, and the viability of the project depended on the structural engineers being able to demonstrate a practicable construction method to the client and local authorities, using models. The erection of the façade on site was achieved without the use of temporary supports. Sections of the structure were lifted into position by crane after pre-assembly at ground level. Once assembled, the façade was fully stable, independently of the pavilion roof that it supports.

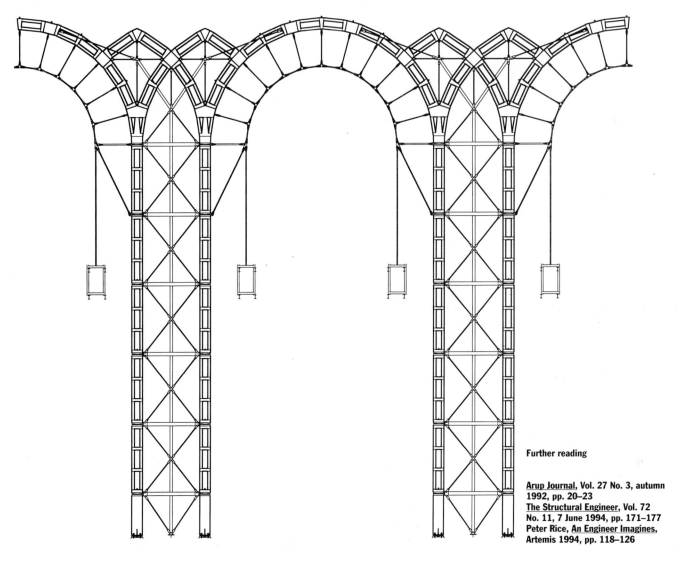

Further reading

Arup Journal, Vol. 27 No. 3, autumn 1992, pp. 20–23
The Structural Engineer, Vol. 72 No. 11, 7 June 1994, pp. 171–177
Peter Rice, An Engineer Imagines, Artemis 1994, pp. 118–126

Design development

Looking at completed buildings, as we have in previous sections, has three serious disadvantages:

- it is all too easy for design to appear like solving brain-teasers – tackling a series of 'problems' that are known to have 'solutions' – rather than as a process in which the problems themselves first need to be established (and to which there may not be feasible solutions);
- it is difficult to convey the interaction and integration of the structural engineer's contribution with the work of other members of the design team: architects, services engineers, specialist contractors, quantity surveyors;
- it is difficult to show design as a process extending over time, developing from the start of a project through to the construction stage (just as it is difficult to get the full flavour of a game of rugby from a few still photographs).

Ideas for different elements of a design arise from many sources and for all sorts of reasons. Some groups of ideas will naturally develop together, feeding off one another; other ideas will be totally incompatible with one another. Some ideas might spark off trains of thought in entirely new directions. Even when the brief is a good one, it, too, is likely to change once design has begun.

Each group of designers will behave and interact during this process in their own unique way – there are no rules or methods to follow. Usually, some members of a design team will have worked together before and ideas from previous projects are likely to re-emerge. Ultimately, it is only the idea of the goal which focuses the group's attention and activity, and early in a project the goal is seldom clearly defined.

So, in one manner or another, designs develop. Early on, many different possibilities will be considered; gradually ideas begin to interlock, at first loosely, then more firmly. Finally, the many different strands of the structural design and the architectural and services design become so integrated and interrelated – so highly engineered – that it becomes virtually impossible to alter one feature without affecting many, if not all the others. It is for this reason that the idea of 'optimisation' is often so meaningless in building design. There are usually several stages during design development after which it is simply not cost-effective to go back and consider significantly different proposals. In the end, good design can only be achieved by employing good designers.

This final section looks at just one project on which, at the time of writing, construction has not yet commenced. We begin with the client's brief and a blank sheet of paper. We see various architectural, structural and services design concepts appear, develop and, sometimes, disappear. We end with a building, designed in all its substantial details and with all the major decisions made about how it will be fabricated and constructed.

Good solutions will emerge if both professions know their job, share the same goals, respect each other and, most importantly, if the involvement of the engineer starts early in the architect's programmatic and conceptual phase. The architect will not get the best results by demanding a structure from an engineer under already fixed and constraining boundary conditions. The architect must be open to a contribution from the engineer, and the engineer must be willing to contribute by proposing alternative structural solutions. Then each must be willing to understand the thinking of the other and to give sufficient explanations of his work to allow for understanding.

Jörg Schlaich

Commerzbank

Frankfurt 1994–1997

Structural engineer Jack Zunz, Chris Wise, Harry Bridges, Peter Bailey, Chris Smith, Sean Walsh, Gabriele Del Mese – <u>Ove Arup & Partners</u>

The designers of the new headquarters building for the Commerzbank were selected on the basis of a limited Ideas Competition. Twelve practices were invited to enter, nine from Germany, two from the USA and Sir Norman Foster & Partners from Britain. Fosters chose to develop their entry with Ove Arup & Partners, largely on the basis of many previous successful collaborations. The brief was distributed on 13 February 1991 and competition entries had to be delivered by 3 June.

The brief and building context

From the first page of the brief it was clear that the client was seeking an unusual, indeed, an innovative building. After the three principal aims of the competition was the embracing requirement that 'die Verträglichkeit der Lösung mit der Umgebung hat gleichen Rang wie der Nutzwert' (the environmental friendliness of the design shall be as important as functional worth). The Commerzbank's mission statement gave other clues to its attitude to the built environment: 'The spirit of a company determines its architecture and its architecture reflects the image of a company'. And, more particularly: 'Wir engagieren uns für umweltverträglichen Fortschritt' (we are committed to environmentally-friendly progress). In this light the Bank was clear about the significance of the new building: 'Through the creation of an ecologically-sound building, we have the chance to portray ourselves as an innovative Bank which takes its social responsibility seriously.

With a building which will stand at the forefront of environmentally-friendly architecture for many years to come, we will display that aspect of the Bank's personality which favourably differentiates us from our competitors.'

Throughout the brief, internal and external environmental issues were mentioned again and again. Despite being a restricted site, there was a requirement to create new green space. There was encouragement to employ 'innovative concepts' and energy-saving systems for the mechanical services. Heating and lighting needs should be reduced, and natural ventilation should be used as much as possible. Even in the high-rise part of the development, fresh-air ventilation was required which could be achieved by opening windows, as long as safety and draught-free airflow was ensured. Similarly, the need for cooling should be reduced by giving adequate protection from the heat and light of the sun.

The building concept should aim to reduce the external envelope to a minimum for the given enclosed volume, achieve an energy-efficient disposition of enclosed volumes, exploit passive heat gain, avoid draughts, minimise disturbance of the ground water level and consider measures such as roof gardens to compensate for area of ground occupied by the building. Even in the construction process itself, the environment should be safeguarded: all construction should be energy saving, building materials and processes should be environmentally friendly, construction waste should be

avoided or recycled, and an energy-saving construction method should be used.

Adopting this broadly 'green' approach was also seen as bringing great commercial benefits by adding to the value of the site, improving the total cost-effectiveness of the building and, by reducing the running and maintenance costs, improving the rentability of the floor space.

Finally, among just four criteria on which the competition entries would be judged, was 'environmental friendliness/approach to energy issues'.

The brief, of course, contained all the more usual prescriptions: the floor area needed, the likely height (about 160 metres) and location of the main entrance, the allowable proximity to the Bank's existing 30-storey building on the same site (both above and below ground), the listed buildings that needed to be protected, and so on. One other matter that received particular mention was the requirement that core floor areas (<u>Kernflächen</u>) must not be concentrated centrally and could serve several floors so that 'a limited number of storeys can be openly linked together'.

Conception – the competition scheme

The response of designers to a brief is a mixture of many things: picking out key ideas from the brief, taking inspiration from the client, the cultural climate or specific aspects of the site and, of course, the designers' own experiences and enthusiasms, as well as ideas based on fundamental principles, clear logic and a consideration of the way materi-

Services Engineers   Dr Michael Schmidt, Klaus Bode, Ian Mulquiney, Graham Cossons, John Perry Roger Preston / Klimasystemtechnik (RP+KSozietät)

Client   <u>Commerzbank AG</u>

als and structures work and can be manufactured.

The shape of the site and the proximity of the existing 30-storey tower clearly favoured a non-rectangular plan, and the idea that it should be triangular came very early. One proposal arose from the need to shield the office floors from solar gain. Common areas and

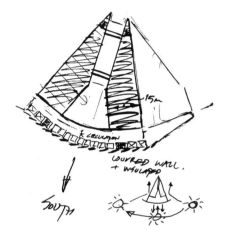

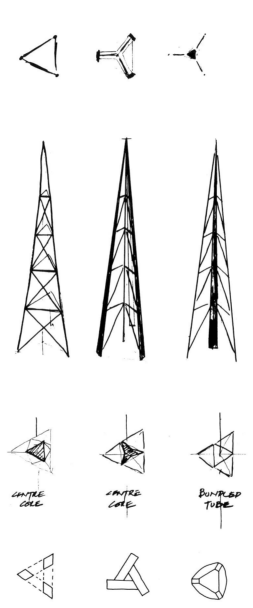

access ways could be on the south face of the building with the office space housed in two wedges. All three sections would be linked to work as a structurally efficient tube.

However, a study of the energy equations soon showed that the main source of heat gain was not the sun but electrical equipment within the building. A wider range of possible high-rise structures was then looked at, all based on a triangular plan and with different ways of achieving sufficient lateral and torsional stability, some in the form of a structural tube, others with a central core.

Inspired, perhaps, by the phrase in the brief about linking groups of floors

together, and the suggestion to consider roof gardens, the idea arose of creating a perforated tube – groups of storeys alternating with garden spaces. A tube was favoured since it is inherently stiffer

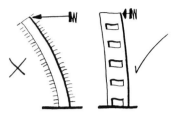

than a central-core scheme (the section has a larger second moment of area in plan).

The problem with such an idea, though, was how to make the structure stiff enough in the storeys with gardens. Cross-bracing would defeat the object of the voids and it would not be feasible to

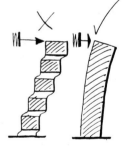

make the columns of a giant Vierendeel frame stiff enough. In a high-rise building the stiffness of the entire building and of each floor has to be carefully limited because of what engineers colloquially refer to as 'the P-delta effect'. If a column sways too far away from the vertical there comes a point when the vertical load (P) which it supports is shifted laterally (δ) to such a degree relative to the base that overturning due to the eccentric load overcomes the column's ability to restore itself to the vertical. To prevent such instability and dramatic collapse, overall sway is limited about 1:500, and single-storey sway to about 1:700.

Then came the flash of inspiration. By having the garden void on just one side of the triangular building, and by rotating this plan up the building, each storey of the building would comprise one garden area and two office areas, and this would enable adequate lateral stiffness to be developed.

Groups of six storeys, which came to be known as villages, would alternate

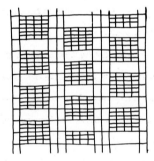

with three-storey-high, glass-walled voids which would enclose the garden areas. The structure of each village could be braced in the plane of the façade using Vierendeel action and serve to link the main vertical structure in the three perimeter towers. Within each village, the frame would reflect the higher bending moments and shear forces near the corner towers due to gravity loads. Towards the main columns, beams would be deeper, and columns wider and closer together. Out of all these structural considerations there was beginning to emerge a powerful architectural image for the visual appearance of the building.

Meanwhile, different ways of bracing

the structure were still being discussed, including tension cross-bracing, trusses and outrigger schemes. Some ideas contained hints of previous Foster/Arup collaborations, including the Hong Kong & Shanghai Bank and the Barcelona Communications Tower. Gradually the idea of using Vierendeel bracing was becoming more firmly established and attention focused on the cores and how they would discharge their several functions: primary load-bearing structure, lateral stability, vertical services distribution leading into horizontal distribution at each storey, vertical transportation and housing the communal areas on each floor.

In parallel with the development of the tower's superstructure, the means of providing it with suitable foundations

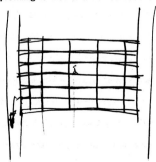

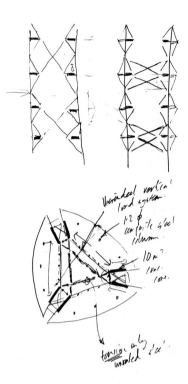

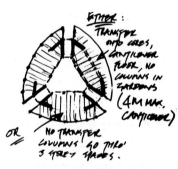

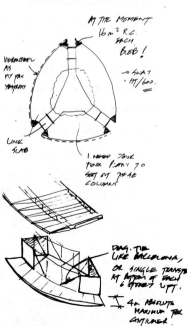

Architect   Spencer de Grey, Ken Shuttleworth, Mark Sutcliffe, John Silver, Tom Politowicz, Brandon Haw, Robin Partington, Paul Kalkhoven, Hans Brouwer, Uwe Nienstedt –

Sir Norman Foster & Partners

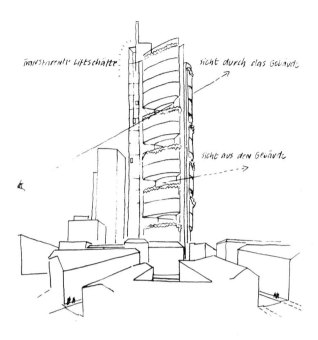

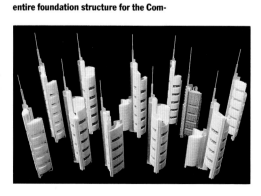

were also being addressed. Frankfurt sits on a bed of clay about 30 metres deep; below this is the Inflata layer which, although it has the characteristics of rock, is a highly irregular succession of limestone, calcerous sand and silt and the occasional layer of clay. It is also permeated by voids, some as large as 2 metres wide. Because of this variability, no building foundations in the city have ever penetrated into the Inflata layer and, consequently, there is no experience of working in it. The initial geotechnical survey therefore included the usual recommendation that the entire foundation structure for the Com-

merzbank should be within the Frankfurt Clay, whose characteristics are well known. It was suggested that the structure should take the form of a raft (to spread the weight over the full area of the site) with piles to control the raft's settlement. Two alternative raft forms were considered: a solid slab 6 metres thick, and a thinner base slab, 2.5 metres thick, stiffened by a grillage of vertical walls three storeys deep. The cellular structure was favoured at this stage as it seemed more likely to fit in with the developing architectural ideas.

The triangular superstructure that was being developed had one particular feature which could only aggravate the difficulty of designing the substructure: the entire weight of the building would be concentrated beneath each of the three towers rather than spread over the whole site. Since it would not be possible to support the towers within the clay layer alone, the only solution was to

devise a transfer structure which would distribute the concentrated loads over the full area of a raft, which could then be piled in the way usual in Frankfurt. Early schemes for the building included three or four levels of basement car parks. These would bring two benefits for the substructure: there would be sufficient depth of basement to effect the redistribution of loads to the raft, and the deep excavation would sufficiently reduce the load on the clay beneath to allow it to carry the weight of the building. On the other hand, the deep basement would leave correspondingly less depth of clay to carry the piles.

It was clear that the overall weight of the building would need to be reduced by every possible means – one designer's question about the weight of door handles was only just a joke. At competition stage, a workable though expensive scheme for the substructure was devised which used a deep, solid raft supported on piles. Nevertheless, it was clear that the new building would need very long piles in a comparatively soft clay and there was concern that the

inevitable settlement of the foundations might threaten adjacent buildings.

As the competition deadline approached, ideas had to converge and the so-called 'fish-tail' option was selected. In this scheme there would be three internal cores at each corner of the triangular plan housing stairs and services risers, while all the lifts would be concentrated in an extension from one corner and ascend on the outside of the building. There had been some talk by the client of future additions to the new building and this separate lift tower would have facilitated this possibility.

In such a tall building it was essential that the floor structure be as thin as possible, and in the office areas between the three towers – the so-called petals – the structural engineers had proposed 16-metre precast-concrete planks spanning between steel beams. The volume occupied by the planks would be used especially efficiently by casting longitudinal voids in the concrete. These would serve as supply and exhaust ducts for the air conditioning. The remaining services would be housed in a deep, raised floor.

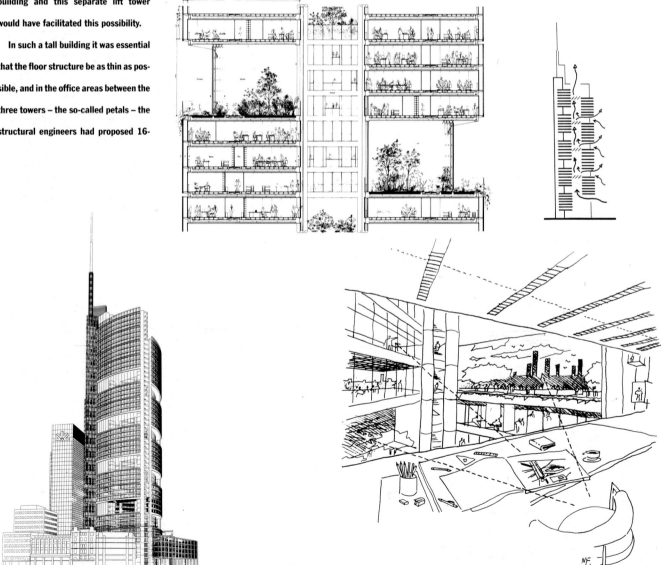

For much of the year the building would be naturally ventilated. To prevent it becoming a 250-metre-tall wind tunnel the full-height atrium was divided into four sections by horizontal glazed screens. Air would flow horizontally through the office floors in the villages, the central void of each nine-storey section, and the gardens. The flow would be limited and adjusted by louvres which would also serve to control smoke in the event of a fire.

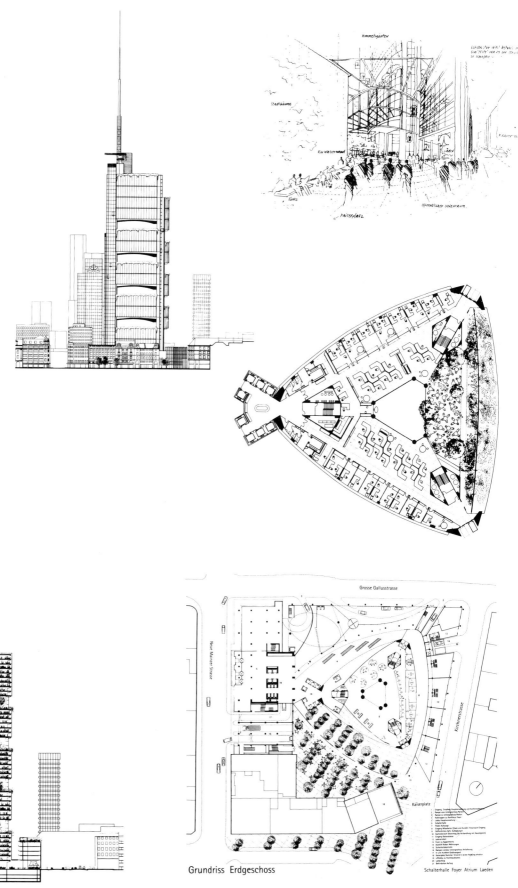

Grundriss Erdgeschoss   Schalterhalle Foyer Atrium Laeden

Design development and integration

The fish-tail scheme was finally selected by the Commerzbank as winner of the Ideas Competition. It was given the go-ahead in late 1991 for further development and final approval in order to secure the necessary building permit.

Further work on the competition scheme exposed some difficulties. The internal structure and services cores were intruding too much on the usable floor space and compromising the ratio of net-to-gross floor areas. Also, the number and location of the lifts were making it difficult to provide suitable vertical transportation. It had been planned to have two sets of lifts: one to serve each six-storey village (arriving at the fourth floor), and others to serve the floors within each village (up two floors and down three).

The response to these problems was to increase the number of lifts in the fish-tail from eight to fourteen, and to reduce the sizes of the cores and move them towards the vertices of the triangular floor plan. But still the scheme was found to have disadvantages. The fish-tail added a large area of building envelope for relatively little enclosed volume. This meant a lot of additional cladding and excessive heat loss in winter, and the location of the lifts and cores meant there were always relatively large distances to walk in any journey between floors.

The shape of the building would also have a serious bearing on the structure. The fins would increase the wind resistance of the building and generate eccentric and torsional loads (both loads would need additional structure to resist them). There were also worries about the proximity of the adjacent building – the fins would be just 5 metres away and such a small gap would lead to very high local wind speeds and negative pressures on adjacent windows. These concerns were not helped by the difficulties below ground level. No matter how carefully the new basements and foundations might be constructed, there was the possibility of disturbing the ground supporting the existing building just a few metres away and affecting its verticality.

And so eventually the fish-tail was abandoned in favour of a three-core solution within a symmetrical plan. Three sets of lifts would serve all floors of the building and the structure and services would be integrated more tightly within the cores to liberate more usable floor space and improve the net-to-gross area ratio. But there were more serious problems ahead.

The client had been collaborating closely and offering encouragement as the original brief evolved to take account of some of the new ideas which had arisen during design development. However, it gradually became clear that the original cost plan was going to be exceeded. Finally, a meeting of the Commerzbank Board decided that the scheme, as it then stood, was too expensive and did not make efficient enough use of the gross floor area.

In response to this decision, and before focusing their efforts to improve the scheme, the building designers undertook a detailed comparison of eight possible versions of the building with different building plans, floor layouts, structural and core details, and servicing and lifting strategies. These were compared with respect to cost, programme time, foundations, ease of construction, net-to-gross efficiency, and environmental issues.

Following this comparative study, the architects set up independent design teams to develop two of the alternative strategies. One team would work on the current scheme with the modified brief and strive to bring it back within budget and make the floor use more efficient. The other team would develop an idea which had been previously discarded – a more conventional scheme with a single, central core with the garden areas at the corners of the triangular plan. The result was a double success. A central-core scheme was developed at considerably less than the original budget and with a better net-to-gross area ratio; and the three-core scheme was also brought back on budget with a better net-to-gross ratio and improved transport strategy. While the central-core scheme was rather cheaper it offered a less attractive solution from the point of view of workplace and environmental issues. The client was by this time sufficiently wedded to the more innovative three-core scheme to favour it, as long as it could be delivered on budget.

The various improvements to the three-core competition scheme were achieved mainly by a change to the building footprint and a number of developments to the building services. The efficiency of floor use was improved by changing the rounded triangular footprint to one with rather flatter faces. The servicing in the competition scheme had used on-floor plant. Although this offered great flexibility, it was hungry on floor space. By centralising the building services into two main plant rooms the core areas of the building could be better exploited and the net-to-gross area ratio improved. The number of storeys in each village was increased from six to eight, and the height of the gardens from three to four storeys. This gained some floor area and enabled the lifting strategy to be improved. The number of full-height lifts was reduced to just two, for the disabled and goods. The other lifts would serve selected floors – one group for floors 1–21, a second for 22–35, and a third for 35–50. The space above and between these short-run lifts was liberated to gain yet more usable floor area.

The reduced number of villages and gardens brought a number of other benefits. More daylight would be brought into the interior of the building and less equipment would be needed to control airflow through the gardens and central void. The new scheme also resulted in a less abrupt top to the building, which the city planners favoured in such a prominent structure.

In general, the existing structural scheme was adaptable enough to accommodate all these various changes with only minor alterations, and the larger size of the villages did permit

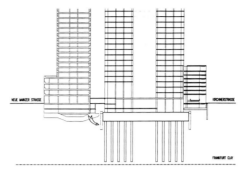

Competition scheme – solid, piled raft

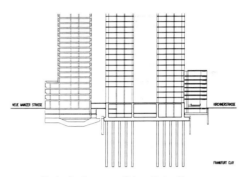

Revised scheme – cellular, piled raft

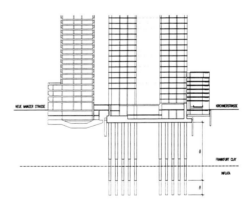

Final scheme – fully piled, no raft

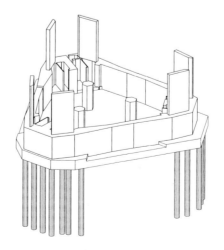

Final scheme

some small reductions in the size, and hence, cost, of the frame structure. However, one of the ways in which the cost of the building was brought back on budget was to have very serious consequences for the design of the foundations.

It had been decided to move the basement car-parking to one of the perimeter buildings in order to reduce the number of basement levels to two beneath the tower and one elsewhere. The foundations of the competition scheme were at the very limit of what could be achieved using a piled raft. Reducing the number of basements would mean that less soil would need to be excavated and the ground beneath would have to carry additional weight; since this would give rise to excessive settlements a piled raft would no longer be feasible. An entirely new foundation structure would have to be devised, one which would be unprecedented in the Frankfurt area.

The first approach was to try to refine the substructure incorporated within the bottom three storeys of the tower, one above and two below ground level. As in the competition scheme, the cellular transfer structure, comprising a grid of 12-metre-deep shear walls, would distribute the loads from the main columns over the full area of soil beneath the tower. However, it was found to be very difficult to make good use of these lower storeys unless a large number of openings were provided through the shear walls; this reduced their structural effectiveness so much that, once again, the foundations could not be made to work at an acceptable cost.

And so the bullet had to be bitten – an answer would have to found at greater depth; piles would have to penetrate the Inflata layer and a whole new world would need to be explored. Once this decision had been made, some tremendous benefits followed. It was quickly recognised that there was no longer any need for the usual raft. The load paths through the foundation could be made significantly simpler and cheaper – loads from the three cores could be carried vertically right down to the piles rather than having to be diverted through 90° into the raft and a further 90° into the piles. Also, since the internal stiffening walls of the cellular raft would now be redundant, they could be removed and free up the interior space in the basements.

Full three-storey-deep stiffening walls were retained in the circumference to give fixity to the feet of the main columns of the tower. And, since the perimeter buildings now had only one basement, the walls of the lower basement beneath the tower would not need to be penetrated by circulation and service routes. This solid 4-metre-deep wall would be able to provide sufficient stiffness to allow the rest of the stiffening walls to be penetrated more freely. the provision of an entire storey of unpenetrated wall had not been possible in the earlier, cellular raft schemes and, with hindsight, this was found to bring much greater flexibility to the planning of services and circulation routes between the

tower and the perimeter buildings on the two storeys above.

As the piles for this foundation scheme would be longer (between 40 and 50 metres) than could be achieved using conventional piling equipment, a new type of pile had to be devised. The main problem would be to overcome friction in the 30 metres of clay when piling at greater depth. The solution was to adopt a step reduction in the pile diameter just above the Inflata layer. An oversize hole was cut through the clay and lined; this allowed the smaller hole to be cut into the Inflata layer without being impeded by friction in the clay above.

With these more fundamental issues dealt with, the process of refining the scheme in all its details and reducing its cost could begin. A computer spreadsheet program was written to perform a large number of 'what-if' tests on the Vierendeel structure of each village to find the best compromise between the ideal forms for gravity loads and wind loads. In this way the maximum feasible stiffness per tonne was extracted from the steel. At the same time the location of the connections between the steel members was considered; by positioning them at or near points of contraflexure (where bending moments are zero) they would need to carry mainly shear loads and could be correspondingly lighter, simpler, cheaper and easier to assemble in situ.

The floor system in the petal areas also needed to be reconsidered. The structural engineers came to realise that stitching each of the concrete floor

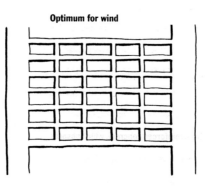

Optimum for wind

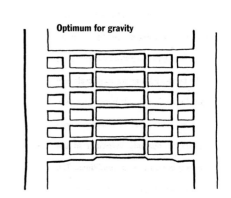

Optimum for gravity

Bending moments and splice locations

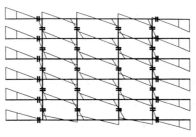

Wind loading

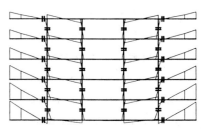

Gravity loading

planks containing air ducts to the main structural frame would require considerable time and effort, which would be correspondingly costly. It was also found that this did not bring the weight advantage which had been anticipated. The engineers proposed an all-steel alternative (a metal decking floor on steel beams) which would be lighter, easier to construct and cheaper. However, even this change was not straightforward. The beams would need to be perforated by a large number of holes to accommodate the air ducts – five or six in a 16-metre length – and this would be too costly. Attention was again focused on the services. The entire system of ventilation and air conditioning was reassessed to design out some of them services and so reduce the number of ducts beneath floors and bring costs back within budget.

This amount of steel in the building brought two problems. The first was cultural: it is still the norm in Germany to make large buildings from concrete and most German contractors were not keen to construct in steel. The second concerned the dynamic behaviour of the building in gusty wind conditions. The building would need to be made stiff enough to ensure the frequency of oscillation, and the accelerations would need to be low enough to be acceptable to occupants. Being an all-steel building, and hence very light, it would be more sensitive to wind loads than a heavier building (the acceleration due to a force varies inversely with the mass). But as this problem is solved by increasing the

stiffness, so the frequency of oscillation increases. There was also the question of damping. Since steel is highly elastic, oscillations of the building caused by wind gusts die down very slowly.

A detailed study was undertaken to

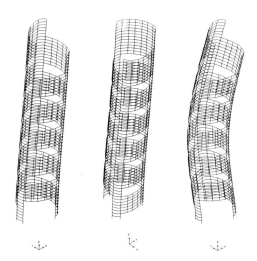

investigate the dynamic behaviour of the structure, both in the direction of the wind and perpendicular to it. The stiffness was adjusted to limit the maximum acceleration in a ten-year period to 1.5 per cent of the acceleration due to gravity – rather less than the recommended levels. Sufficient damping was introduced into the building by making the main load-bearing columns in the cores from reinforced concrete, which absorbs much more energy than steel when it vibrates. The concrete would also encase the steel corner columns of the Vierendeel frames, and shear studs welded to the columns would ensure composite action with the concrete.

The client still had reservations about the all-steel structural scheme, partly because of the preference for concrete in Germany. To satisfy these concerns, an all-concrete alternative was prepared

on lines similar to the current steel design. It was found that the vertical elements of the Vierendeels would need to be nearly 2 metres wide and nearly half the window area would be lost. The building would also be some 20 per cent heavier and no cost-effective foundation could be devised which would carry this weight. A concrete version of the building would simply not be feasible.

The construction method devised by the structural engineers will have minimum impact on the environment and be as cost-effective as possible. Below ground, matters will be dominated by the nature of the soil and the Inflata layer beneath, the proximity of the adjacent building and the high water table, which must not be disturbed. Concrete piles cast inside temporary casings will be used in preference to the less environmentally-friendly Bentonite. Vertical and horizontal movement of the soft clay soil will be minimised by undertaking a ballasted excavation of the site – as soil is removed, the surface will be surcharged with new construction to maintain soil pressures and prevent heave. By this means the foundations of the adjacent high-rise building and several listed buildings will be protected.

Above ground the entire design of the structure has been conceived with rapid and cheap construction in mind. Only the nine triangular steel columns and the small frames linking each pair of concrete columns change in size down the building. The rest of the structure is virtually identical at every floor level throughout the 250-metre height. Even the six main reinforced-concrete columns are of constant external dimensions – their increasing strength and stiffness is achieved by adjusting the internal reinforcement.

This repetition is made possible because the building is braced by Vierendeel action – it resists wind loads by shearing rather than bending. Hence the resistance to wind is shared more or less equally by the structure at each floor level rather than progressively

accumulating in the columns towards ground level (as is the case in a building which resists wind by bending). The floor and Vierendeel structure of each village is designed, first and foremost, as a kit of parts to facilitate easy construction. Steelwork will be cut, drilled, welded and prefabricated in factory conditions, with as few different components and sub-assemblies as possible. All connections are made with friction grip bolts to avoid site welding. It has thus been possible to

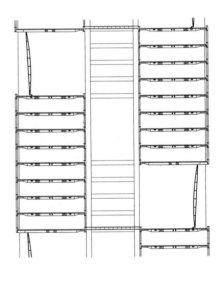

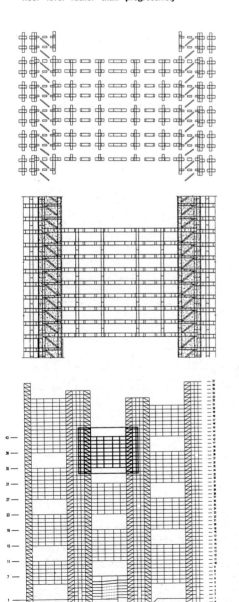

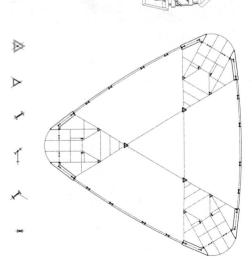

achieve an unprecedented degree of standardisation in such a tall building.

Design of the new Commerzbank headquarters was substantially complete by the end of 1993, some 24 months after the competition had been won. The scheme that has resulted from the imaginative brief is a highly-engineered building which, to quote one of its designers, 'breaks all the rules'. For a building of its height and type, many of its features are highly original:

- it carries gravity and wind loads in an innovative way;
- the office space is entirely column-free;
- the weight of the entire building (52–61 storeys, about 100,000 tonnes) is just two-thirds that of the adjacent 30-storey block (about 150,000 tonnes);
- its fully piled basement is unique and of unprecedented depth in Frankfurt;
- the structure has a highly repetitive kit of parts and sub-assemblies with standardised dimensions and connections;
- it is the first major steel building in Germany;
- it is the first major high-rise building in Germany with dry walling;
- the floor utilisation is very high – each floor accommodates 60 office units at 15 square metres per person;
- its shape in plan provides very large window areas for the site and floor area;
- all the offices are naturally lit;
- the building affords striking views from both the inside and ground level;
- while being a large building it does not appear as a monolithic block and its entrance is in harmony with the scale of the surrounding buildings;
- for about nine months of the year it is naturally ventilated;
- the gardens bring fresh air quality right to the top of the building.

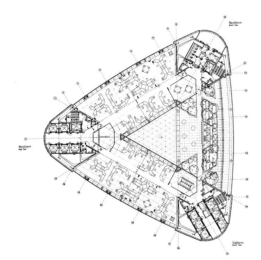

Annotated bibliography

Addis, William, Structural Engineering: the Nature of Theory and Design (Ellis Horwood, 1990).

A discussion of the nature of structural engineering design as an activity, an art undertaken by skilled people, looking at how it has been, or might have been, done during the last 3000 years. It looks at the nature of progress in engineering and the contribution which engineering science ('theory') has played in the work of the design engineer. Philosophy and history are mixed with much discussion of design. Includes an extensive bibliography.

Arup, Ove, 'The Engineer and the Architect', Proceedings of the Institution of Civil Engineers, Vol. 13, 1958–59, pp. 503–510; discussion pp. 510–532.

One of Ove Arup's best discussions of his philosophies. In particular he puts forward his idea of 'total design' at a time when most engineers and architects were inclined to live separate lives.

Billington, David, The Tower and the Bridge (Princeton University Press, 1985).

The book traces what the author claims is 'the new art of structural engineering' (the book's subtitle), from Telford through to the present day. It is a brief but excellent introduction to many of the structural engineers whose work is worth scrutiny, though the impact of the book is reduced by uninspiring black and white photographs. Many useful references.

Brawne, Michael, Arup Associates: the Biography of an Architectural Practice (Lund Humphries, 1983).

The story of the unique building design practice born out of Ove Arup's vision of 'total design'. Project teams comprising structural and services engineers, architects, quantity surveyors and interior designers work together in the ultimate multidisciplinary environment. The result has been a series of highly innovative buildings of many different types.

Cottam, David, Owen Williams (Architectural Association, 1986).

Williams was one of Britain's few acknowledged engineer/architects who exploited the richness and versatility of concrete. As an engineer, he is remembered for the buildings at the Wembley British Empire Exhibition (1924), and as an engineer/architect for several memorable buildings during the 1930s – the Dorchester Hotel, the Empire Pool at Wembley, the Peckham Health Centre, the Boot's and Daily Express buildings. He also designed the first bridges on the M1 motorway.

Deswarte, Sylvie and Bertrand Lemoine, L'Architecture et les Ingénieurs: deux siècles de construction (Editions du Moniteur, 1980).

This richly illustrated book appeared in conjunction with an exhibition at the Centre Beaubourg in Paris. Includes sections on long-span roofs, bridges, tunnels, dams, towers and other miscellaneous structures. Many familiar friends here, but a lot of comparative strangers. The text begins with the question 'Qu'entend-on par "art de l'ingénieur"?', and the rest of the book proceeds to provide answers.

'Engineering & Architecture', Architectural Design Profile 70, Architectural Design, Vol. 57, November/December 1987.

A special issue celebrating the engineer's contribution to architecture. Several thought-provoking essays from Ted Happold, Charles Jencks, Jack Zunz, Robert Thorne and Derek Walker, amongst others, and photo-essays on a number of current projects.

Ferguson, Eugene S, Engineering and the Mind's Eye (MIT Press, 1992).

A rare attempt by a philosopher/historian to study what it is to be a design engineer. Episodes from many branches of engineering over many centuries make a good read and offer a wide range of insights to the designer's world.

Foster, Michael (ed.), The Principles of Architecture: Style, Structure and Design (New Burlington Books, 1982).

Although 'just another coffee-table architecture book', this one is unusual in acknowledging the importance of engineering and building technology. An excellent introduction to what building design and construction is all about, using both historical and modern examples.

Bridging the Gap: Rethinking the Relationship of Architect and Engineer (Van Nostrand Reinhold, 1991).

Much has been written on this subject – too much perhaps. By reading this volume you will avoid the need to look more widely for it contains nine excellent essays and some discussion by people who have something interesting to say. The book is a record of a symposium at the Guggenheim Museum involving three engineers (Peter Rice, Jörg Schlaich, William LeMessurier,), two architects (Richard Rogers, Richard Keating of SOM), one sculptor/architect/engineer (Santiago Calatrava) and three philosopher-observers of design (Peter McCleary, Tom Peters, David Billington).

Harris, Alan, 'Architectural Misconceptions of Engineering', RIBA Journal, February 1961, pp. 130–136.

Stimulating wisdom. If all engineers and architects had read this and heeded its messages, the world (of architecture) would be a better place.

Holgate, Alan, The Art in Structural Design (Clarendon Press, 1986).

This is a useful and thought-provoking 'introduction and sourcebook' for both students and teachers of architecture and engineering. Despite the title, it treats neither the visual nor craft aspects of structural engineering, but rather, the broad context in which structural design takes place. Contains a useful bibliography.

Kipling, Rudyard, 'The Ship That Found Herself' (from the collection A Day's Work).

The only example I know of structural engineering written from the point of view of the structure! The wrought-iron plates and rivets of a ship tell their own story of the stresses and strains of surviving an Atlantic storm. In the same volume, 'The Bridge Builder' is another rare example of engineering in literature.

Mainstone, Roland, Developments in Structural Form (MIT Press, 1975).
A wonderful overview and reference work on the historical development of construction materials and forms and the emergence of engineering science as the designer's tool. Very well illustrated and few important buildings or structures are overlooked. An excellent source of references to the historical literature, though not presented in an easy-to-find way. Currently out of print.

Nervi, Pier Luigi, Aesthetics and Technology in Building (Harvard University Press, 1966).
A record of his remarkable buildings in concrete – in-situ, precast and ferrocemento, the material he invented. A lot of good philosophy and engineering comes across in discussion of both his own works and the classics. *Structures* (F W Dodge, 1956) is a rarer work, a translation of his 'Scienza o arte del construire?' (1945).

Petroski, Henry, To Engineer is Human (Macmillan, 1985).
Successfully addresses the question 'What do engineers do?' Many of the anecdotes relate to buildings and structures, including the lessons to be learnt from the collapse at the Hyatt Regency Hotel in 1981. An easy read, but the UK edition lacks pictures.

Pirsig, Robert M, Zen and the Art of Motorcycle Maintenance (Bodley Head, 1974).
Surely one of the best book titles ever. In charting a voyage of personal and psychological discovery, the author builds upon the engineering skills he has acquired and the relationship between his intellectual and physical experience of materials and mechanics.

Rice, Peter and Hugh Dutton, Le Verre structurel (Editions du Moniteur, 1990).
The full story of the 32 x 32 metre glass wall at La Villette designed by RFR. It charts the road of discovery which led to using glass as a structural material (in tension), and there is no better exposition of the principles of bracing façades for wind loading.

Rice, Peter, An Engineer Imagines (Artemis, 1994).
Peter Rice was a rare example of a structural engineer who had the desire to explain what he thought and did, and the ability of a raconteur to communicate it to others. In this autobiography, he combines the stories of several projects, including Sydney Opera House, Centre Beaubourg, Menil Art Gallery and the IBM travelling exhibition, with his philosophy of design.

Sabbagh, Karl, Skyscraper: the Making of a Building (Macmillan, 1989).
Written in conjunction with a four-hour TV series to chart the full story of the conception, design and construction of Worldwide Plaza in New York. Not since the Crystal Palace has there been such a record of a building's creation – a gripping read for anyone.

Sandaker, Bjorn S and Arne P Eggen, The Structural Basis of Architecture (Phaidon, 1993).
A remarkable book in that it puts over the principles of structure in a way that appeals to architects (even including a few equations). Line drawings with arrows (ubiquitous in such books) are, for a change, brought alive by frequent illustrations of classic buildings and structures.

Strike, James, Construction into Design: the Influence of New Methods of Construction on Architectural Design 1690–1990 (Butterworth-Heinemann, 1991).
The only book successfully to link the world of production engineering and manufacturing technologies with the work of the building designer.

'The Architecture of New Engineering', double issue of Casabella, Nos. 542/543, January/February 1988.
A unique collection of essays about structural engineering and architecture and reflections on the significance of a range of projects. Essays by philosophers, historians and engineers, including Reyner Banham, Kenneth Frampton, Frank Newby, Ove Arup, Antoine Picon, Edoardo Benvenuto. In Italian, with brief summaries in English.

Torroja, Eduardo, The Philosophy of Structures (University of California Press, 1967).
Still the classic in this field, but unfortunately long out of print. Torroja was a rare combination of imaginative engineer and someone who could abstract generalities from his own particular experiences and present them as the principles which guided his engineering life. Although written in the golden age of concrete and shells, he talks equally passionately about steel and timber, and all manner of structural forms. This book is unique amongst the writings of engineers in not focusing on his own works. For those, the reader should go to *The Structures of Eduardo Torroja* (F Dodge Corporation, 1958). For one of the most remarkable uses of a thin concrete shell, try his Pont de Suert church.

Vicenti, Walter G, What Engineers Know and How They Know It: Analytical Studies in Aeronautical Engineering (1990).
Just what the title suggests; the case studies take the reader far beyond the naive, popular idea that designing is inventing. The story of the development of the best shape for rivets in aircraft wings is memorable.

Acknowledgements

I am grateful, most of all, to the many engineers and firms who have given their time and energy to help me tell something of the history of their buildings; without their enthusiasm there would be no book. However, any errors in the text are mine, not theirs. I am also grateful to the University of Reading for allowing me time to compile the book. Finally, special thanks are due to Tess and Orlando, who were so patient every time I disappeared off to the computer to do yet another bit of book; and a word of welcome to Oscar, whose premature arrival made the last few months' work rather more hectic than I would have preferred.

Illustration credits
Where appropriate, illustrations are credited from left to right and from top to bottom of each page.

pages 9–22: Bill Addis, except page 7 extreme right, Ove Arup & Partners; page 10 extreme right, Beat Kasper; page 18 top, Horst Berger; extreme right, Peter Durant; page 19 top right, OAP; second from right, Heini Schneebeli

page 24: photograph Martin Jones; drawings Buro Happold

page 25: Buro Happold

pages 26–27: Buro Happold

page 28: photograph Peter Cook; drawings Price & Myers

pages 29, 30: Buro Happold

page 31: drawing Bill Addis; photograph Buro Happold

page 32: drawing Tony Hunt; photograph YRM-Anthony Hunt Associates

page 33: computer images Mike Barnes; photographs YRM-AHA

page 34: photographs YRM-AHA; Jeremy Cockayne; Tony Woodcock, D.B.S. Graphics; YRM-AHA; drawing YRM-AHA

page 35: Harris & Sutherland; Bill Addis; MacCormac Jamieson Prichard & Wright; Harris & Sutherland; Phil Cooper

page 36: photographs Ben Johnson; drawings Bill Addis

page 37: Chris Wise; Ben Johnson

page 38: Bill Addis

pages 40, 41: drawings Bill Addis; photographs Doug Allan, British Antarctic Survey

pages 42, 43: Arup Associates

page 44: Crispin Boyle, Arup Associates; Arup Assocates; Arup Associates

page 45: Peter Mackinven

page 46: OAP; OAP; Richard Davies

page 47: photographs Bill Addis; drawing OAP

pages 48, 49: Peter Mackinven, OAP

page 50: drawings Marc Mimram; photographs Bill Addis

page 51: Marc Mimram; Bill Addis; photographs Bill Addis

page 52: Bill Addis; Buro Happold; Michael Hopkins & Partners; Buro Happold; Buro Happold; Michael Hopkins & Partners

page 53: drawings Bill Addis; photograph Buro Happold

page 54: Bill Addis; Bill Addis; Bill Addis; Buro Happold; Buro Happold

page 56: photographs Valode et Pistre et Associés; OAP; Bill Addis

page 57: Mike Banfi; Valode et Pistre et Associés; Mike Banfi

pages 58, 59: photographs Curtins Consulting Engineers; drawings Bill Addis

page 60: YRM-AHA; Laing Management Limited

page 61: Peter Cook, YRM-AHA

pages 62–65: photographs Bill Addis; drawings Buro Happold

page 66: photograph Bill Addis; drawings Atelier One

page 67: Atelier One; Alison Brooks, Ron Arad Associates; Bill Addis; Bill Addis; Bill Addis

page 68: Bill Addis

page 69: Ian Lambot

page 70: Bill Addis; Ben Johnson; OAP

page 72: Peter Mackinven; OAP; Bill Addis

page 73: drawings OAP; photograph Bill Addis

pages 74, 75: photographs Tom Schollar; drawing Bill Addis

page 76: photographs Ian Macdonald; drawings Max Fordham & Partners

page 77: photograph Ian Macdonald; drawing Bill Addis

pages 78–80: Arup Associates, except tartan grid Bill Addis, and last picture Crispin Boyle, Arup Associates

page 81: Owens Corning

page 82: Buro Happold; Dennis Gilbert

page 83: Ben Morris; Buro Happold; Dennis Gilbert; Buro Happold

pages 84, 85: photographs Peter Cook; drawing Short Ford and Associates

page 86: Short Ford Associates; Short Ford Associates; Bill Addis; YRM-AHA

page 88: Kurt Gahler

page 89: Robert Keiser; Kurt Gahler

page 90: drawings Price & Myers; photographs Martin Charles

page 91: drawings Price & Myers; photographs Heini Schneebeli

page 92: drawings Price & Myers; photographs Heini Schneebeli

pages 93–95: Bill Addis

page 96: Ian Howarth of Focal Point

page 97: David Tasker; Travers Morgan

pages 98, 99: Studio d'ingegneria: Favero – Milan

page 100: Tony Copeland; Professor Heinz Isler; Tony Copeland; Bill Addis; Tony Copeland

page 101: Tony Copeland; Professor Heinz Isler; Tony Copeland; Bill Addis

page 102: drawings Buro Happold; photograph Robert Thorne

page 103: Buro Happold; Jorg Gribl; Mike Barnes

page 104: Buro Happold; Mike Bill addisrnes

page 106: YRM-AHA; Dennis Gilbert

page 107: YRM-AHA; Bill Addis; Dennis Gilbert

pages 108, 109: OAP

page 110: Heini Schneebeli; Bill Addis; Price & Myers

page 111: Bill Addis; Nicholas Grimshaw & Partners; Jo Reid and John Peck; YRM-AHA

page 112: Bill Addis

page 113: drawings Nicholas Grimshaw & Partners; photograph Peter Strobel

page 114: OAP; Peter Mackinven, OAP

page 115: Jane Richardson; OAP

page 116: OAP/Bill Addis; OAP

page 118: Bill Addis; Peter Mackinven; OAP

page 119: Peter Mackinven

pages 120, 121: photographs Bill Addis; drawing Dewhurst Macfarlane

pages 122, 123: Buro Happold

page 124: Bill Addis

page 125: Phil Cooper

page 126: photographs Bill Addis; drawing OAP

page 127: Bill Addis; Alistair Lenczner; OAP; Bruce Danziger

page 128: OAP

page 131: Chris Wise; Chris Wise; OAP; OAP

page 132: Chris Wise

page 133: photographs Richard Davies; sketch Sir Norman Foster

page 134, 135: photograph Richard Davies; drawings Sir Norman Foster & Partners; sketches Sir Norman Foster

pages 137–139: OAP

page 140: elevation and section Sir Norman Foster & Partners; other drawings OAP

page 141: Sir Norman Foster & Partners; Sir Norman Foster & Partners; Richard Davies